The Best Present Ever

Poems, Stories And Reflections For Christmas

by

Helen M. Clarke

This book is dedicated to Graham Webb (1929-2020), a truly inspirational man. He gave me endless encouragement and support, even finding tunes for some of my poems so that we could sing them. On special occasions he would ask me, with a twinkle in his eye, "Can you feel a poem coming on?" – and whenever I do "feel a poem coming on" I think about Graham and it makes me smile. Thank you, Graham.

Contents

1. George's Expedition

Now let's be clear he wasn't vain
His ego wasn't big
But George the Penguin felt the urge
To find a higher twig
They'd hung him on a branch low down
Which really wasn't fair
The dog kept sniffing round him and
He didn't like it there
A tickly piece of tinsel
Wafted round and round his face
A gaudy bauble blocked his view
He didn't have much space
And so he hatched a daring plan
To scramble to the top
Who knew what thrills awaited him?
He'd climb and wouldn't stop
The tinsel wasn't strong enough
To aid his bold ascent
He wasn't *all* that heavy but
One tug and down he went
He landed on a dove, to which
He clung with all his might
Then paused to calm his jitters and
Recover from the fright
He scanned the scene above him and
Felt hopeful - then quite sure
The flex that held the fairy lights
Was hardy and secure
George stretched up tall and grabbed a bulb
Yikes! That was rather hot!
It seemed the lights were not the means
To reach a better spot

… But what was that? An icicle
He grappled it with poise
It clanked against a trinket but
It didn't make *much* noise
George hauled himself up gracefully
Wow! This was proving fun
He'd made a start. No going back
His journey had begun
He tugged another icicle
And then a sturdy bell
It swayed and tinkled prettily
- And helped him up as well
Then George became adventurous
And bounced on something soft
And though it made him nauseous
It hurtled him aloft
The branches seemed much denser now
And easier to hold
Then George espied the pinnacle
And on it something gold
He scrambled through the upper boughs
And scaled a gleaming star
George wedged himself against it and
Gazed round him, near and far
He'd missed so much while down below
How splendid! All that space!
Yes, this would suit him perfectly
He'd found his rightful place

2. Keeping It Simple

Celia looked down her *To Do* list and sighed. Christmas was getting out of hand.

She did a quick calculation. Postage had gone up since last Christmas. If she bought stamps for all the cards that couldn't be delivered by hand it would cost her a fortune. In fact she wouldn't have any money left for anything else.

Well, okay, that was a slight exaggeration, but the financial outlay for Christmas had become ridiculous.

There were so many presents to buy – and choose, of course, which could be stressful in itself. There were so many cards to purchase, write and send ... and there was so much food to get in ... and there were so many extra activities and social events to pay for and find the time and energy to indulge in.

Was it worth it?

Celia thought not. This year she would keep it simple. She would not be pressured into running herself ragged and rendering herself almost insolvent. She would celebrate Christmas in a quiet, gentle, inexpensive way, and enjoy it all the more for doing so.

She would keep it simple.

And she would begin by pruning her outrageously long Christmas card list.

She crossed off the names of people with whom she had had little contact in recent years. Increasing numbers of cards were being sent out just for the sake of it, she felt certain. Neither party could really be bothered anymore, but neither party wanted to be the one to end the ritual and therefore experience the embarrassment of receiving a card from someone who wasn't going to get one back.

Instead of *exchanging* cards with almost forgotten acquaintances this year, Celia would put herself in the unenviable role of instigating a break with tradition that would subject her to the relentless mortification – just thinking about it that way she could feel herself weakening – of opening card after card from some poor soul who wouldn't be hearing from her.

It would be uncomfortable the first time, she told herself firmly, but it would benefit everyone – and cause considerable relief all round – in the long run.

She hoped people wouldn't assume that she had died. Celia brushed the idea aside. Over-analysing it would just complicate things unnecessarily, and she was supposed to be keeping Christmas simple.

In reality people probably wouldn't even notice that she hadn't sent them a card. The former recipients who had been chopped off the list were not going to be holding Celia at the fronts of their minds.

The next job was to shorten the Christmas gift list.

That would be a harsh thing to do and Celia felt a stab of guilt. No, she couldn't suddenly stop giving presents. The names on this list were not distant associates. These were people she knew well and with whom she had an on-going relationship of some kind.

Okay, she wouldn't remove anyone from the list. She would simply curb her spending. She would tighten her gift buying budget. Everyone would still get a present, but it would cost less than in previous years. It was the thought that counted anyway.

The other issue was the business of decorations. Although they looked pretty and she enjoyed having plenty around, they were tedious and time-consuming to put up. So she would keep the decorations simple as well, limiting herself to Christmas cards and a modestly adorned Christmas tree. Fairy lights plus a few baubles and a bit of tinsel slung around should do the trick.

Yes, this Christmas she would keep it simple.

Her first two Christmas cards were from people still on her list, which gave Celia a feeling of triumph and hope. She had made the right decision and, quite possibly, some of her rejects had omitted her too and would thereby spare her the awkwardness of not reciprocating.

However her satisfaction was short-lived as her next three cards were from people she had axed. One sender even included a little note, for the first time in years, instead of just signing the card.

How are you doing? We must have a catch-up sometime. I'd love to hear from you. This was followed by the correspondent's own news.

Celia steeled herself to ignore the plea, but it was no use. She would have to write back, if not with a Christmas card then at least early in the New Year.

A few days later she received another card with an unexpected message in it, also from someone no longer on her list. How could she not respond? It would be rude and unfriendly. And if she was going to reply, she might as well do so in a Christmas card rather than start up again in a few weeks' time, even if doing so would give away the fact that she had received *their* cards before writing *hers*.

But how could she snub some people and not others? Was it fair to make such a big decision based on the presence or absence of a couple of scrawled extra sentences?

No. She couldn't do it. She reverted to her original list.

Next year she would cull it. *This* year she would keep things simple by sending cards to *everyone*.

She could still cut down on the decorations and curb her spending on gifts and turn down invitations to social events.

She could still keep it simple.

Next day she went shopping for bargains and was delighted with the results of her careful browsing. She managed to buy eight major presents for less than she would usually pay for two.

Buoyed by the success of her shopping expedition, Celia indulged in a quick cup of coffee and then dug out her Christmas tree and boxes of decorations.

She kept it simple, as planned, but even being minimalist about decorating the tree tried her patience. Even keeping it simple was irritating beyond measure. She really did not enjoy putting up

11

decorations. How right she had been when she vowed not to bother much!

At last it was finished. She stood back to admire her handiwork and was bitterly disappointed.

How boring! How plain! What a let-down!

She rooted around in one of her boxes and fished out the jolly Father Christmas … and the cheerful robin … and the dainty little bells, and added them to the sparsely scattered baubles and tinsel.

It was still rather bare. It needed a few more baubles. And some lametta. And those tiny felt stockings she bought at a Christmas Fair a few years ago. And those strings of miniature parcels.

That was better.

Celia checked the time and was horrified at how long it had taken her to sling a few simple decorations around.

She studied the room. There was nothing to say *Christmas* apart from the tree. It wasn't very festive at all.

She fixed a few Christmas cards in strategic positions, but soon realised she wasn't going to be satisfied until she had draped her spare set of fairy lights around the mantel piece, accompanied of course by the faux foliage she always put with it.

An hour later the room was looking bright and Christmassy. She had done a good job – but she hadn't kept it simple, not by any stretch of the imagination.

Never mind. Next year she could plan it in advance and come up with something simple and quick but effective and pretty.

After tea Celia sorted through her bag of bargain gifts. She really was pleased with those. They were good quality items. Nobody would guess how little she had spent on them.

Unless they frequented the same shops as Celia did, of course. What a nasty thought!

Celia's heart lurched. Everyone probably *did* frequent the same shops as she did. Everyone would have been aware of all those exciting gifts that were on offer. Everyone would know what a cheapskate she had been.

Celia groaned. There was nothing for it. She would have to buy some extra goodies to go with the cut-price ones. She couldn't have people believing she was stingy.

Next year she would allow herself time to find bargain gifts that were more obscure, maybe from a catalogue or an online shop. Next year she would keep her shopping inexpensive – and simple. Meanwhile there would be nothing inexpensive or simple about searching around for extra bits to add to an already perfect present just for the sake of spending more money.

Celia was disgusted with herself, but could see no alternative if she didn't want to feel humiliated.

She could still keep the food simple and avoid premature Christmas dinners and time-consuming social events. Surely *that* remained within her power.

Two days later Celia had a phone call from a friend inviting her to a Christmas lunch party, from 12noon to approximately 3pm.

She declined without hesitation, having already rehearsed her excuse. She had something else on. She wouldn't be available. It wasn't a blatant lie, she reassured herself. She didn't need to specify *what* she had on, and she was bound to be doing *something* during that time.

"Oh, can't you change your plans?" pleaded her friend. "Surely you can rearrange things."

Celia sighed irritably. Why couldn't people take *No* for an answer?

"Not really," she muttered with an unwelcome prick of conscience.

"*Please!*" persisted the caller. "It's for Sue. You know what a bad time she's been having, and she suddenly got a big yearning to share a Christmas meal with her friends. It'll mean such a lot to her if you can come."

How could Celia resist a request like that?

"Okay," she agreed reluctantly. "How much will it cost?"

The price was exorbitant.

"Just for a meal?" she exclaimed before she could stop herself.
The caller chuckled.

"No. There are extra trimmings thrown in as well because it's a party," she explained. "It'll be great. You'll enjoy it. And it'll mean so much to Sue."

So that was that. Celia was not going to keep Christmas simple. Not this year anyway.

She shrugged off her frustration and smiled.

Next year she would keep it simple! Hopefully.

3. Christmas Is Cancelled

This Christmas is cancelled
It won't go ahead
It's off. It won't happen. It's banned
No presents, no carols
No parties, no fun
Forget any pleasures you've planned

Traditions don't matter
Emotions don't count
Prepare for a sad, soulless day
Be strong and accept it
Self-pity won't help
Just do as you're told. Just obey …

… Yet Christmas *can* happen
If that is our wish
There's internet, video, phone
It *can* still be joyful
We *can* show we care
By contacting someone alone

My Christmas *will* happen
I'll make sure it does
I don't feel I have much to lose
I'll listen to carols
And trim up my tree
And hand out some gifts if I choose

Yes, Christmas *will* happen
It *will* go ahead
Whatever we feel we can't do
It's still Jesus' birthday
Rejoiced in or not
Its message of love still shines through

Can Christmas be vetoed?
Can Christmas be banned?
To cancel it seems rather odd
We might not observe it
But one thing I know
- We can't *cancel* Christmas. Ask God!

4. A Robin's View Of Christmas

I have finally worked out what Christmas is all about and I have to say I am finding it rather exciting. I had been puzzling over its significance for some time, but could not proceed beyond the observation that it was a big celebration characterised by raucous human behaviour, bright lights and special food. There did not appear to be any particular rationale behind the festivities and that troubled me.

Even more disturbing was the knowledge that the aforementioned raucous human behaviour would – and always will - have to be borne with fortitude as, sadly, it cannot be prevented. Special food, thankfully, extends sporadically to garden residents and so is welcome. Regrettably the blackbirds, sparrows and starlings are also aware of this supplementary bounty and are extremely ill-mannered in their determination to devour excessive quantities, averse as they are to sharing nourishment with the more refined among us.

The extra outdoor lights, although alluring, are actually quite confusing for birds of low intellect, giving these inferior creatures the false impression that it is daytime when, in reality, it is the middle of the night. Christmas lights pose no problem to me, of course. I am an early riser and a late rooster, and I have no difficulty differentiating between sun, moon and artificial light. Other birds are less discerning.

However I digress. This morning I had taken a modest fragment of suet to a window ledge in an attempt to evade the covetous beak of a marauding blackbird when I inadvertently glanced into the room on the other side of the pane. To my immense surprise, joy and delight, I espied multifarious pictures of robins displayed in attractive arrangements around the walls and on items of furniture. Admittedly, there were other images as well, but robins predominated and were clearly the principal players. This was my epiphany.

In that wonderful moment I realised that Christmas is a celebration of *The Robin*. My heart was warmed. My red breast pulsated with pride. I felt almost humbled. How gratifying to discover that humans, wild and raucous though they be, appreciate and revere *The Robin* to such a degree that they will dedicate several weeks of each year to fêting us.

I can only conclude that *Christmas* is an exclusive name for *Robin Adoration*. Suffice it to say I approve.

5. Waiting
(*Advent*)

Am I waiting for His coming?
Am I thinking of His birth?
Will I understand its meaning
For a deeply troubled earth?

Am I open to His message?
Will I take it to my heart?
Will I grow in loving kindness
Pray for peace and play my part?

Am I ready for His Coming?
Am I conscious of my need?
Will I feel His holy presence
In a world of sin and greed?

6. The Big Secret

The grown-ups were being mysterious and secretive and, what was more, they were thoroughly enjoying being mysterious and secretive. The children knew they were up to something. They guessed it was to do with the forthcoming Christmas party at church, but the adults were being so cagey that the children couldn't get any hints at all as to what was going on.

The church held a Christmas party every year and it always followed the same pattern. The older children, with several years' experience behind them, were familiar with this pattern and knew exactly what to expect.

The party would begin with chatting and games. Then there would be food round tables and, of course, lots more chatting. Then, when they had finished eating, they would sing carols until they were hoarse. People would be invited to request their favourites and it would all be very happy. The evening would end with a prayer.

So what was different this year? Why wouldn't the grown-ups tell them what they were planning? It was obviously a surprise. A nice surprise. Something exciting. But *what*?

If they publicised it, the thrill of a special treat would encourage people to come. So why didn't they publicise it? Why were they being mysterious and secretive?

Was it a visit from Santa?

The children thought not. Playgroup and Toddlers always booked Santa for their Christmas parties. It wouldn't be *such* a big surprise if he turned up at the church party as well.

No, it wasn't Santa. It was something a bit more unusual. Something the organisers were very pleased with themselves about. Did *all* the adults know, or just the ones responsible for the arrangements?

The children tried eavesdropping. Maybe they would overhear a conversation that would give them a few clues, if not actually reveal the whole plot.

One of them came very close to finding something out.

"I heard them going on about not mentioning a special surprise at all so that we can get an unexpected thrill when it suddenly happens," he reported to his fellow sleuths.

He looked downcast for a moment.

"Actually, I feel like I've nearly spoilt it," he confessed. "We already know more than they wanted us to. Let's not try and find out what it is."

The other children agreed, suddenly acutely aware that they really didn't want to uncover the secret and ruin the surprise.

On the Sunday before the party, after the morning service, when the members of the congregation were relaxing with cups of tea, coffee and squash and munching biscuits, the lady in charge of party arrangements rapped on her table with a spoon and called for attention.

She reminded everyone about the party and which day it was going to happen and what time it would start.

"And there will be lots of games and lots of yummy food and lots of carols," she trilled. "And plenty of opportunity to natter and have lots of fun. So *do* come."

She paused to catch her breath, beaming round happily at the assembled group.

"What time's the magician coming?" called the minister from the doorway.

"SHUSH!" came an anguished chorus, accompanied by dismayed expressions on a number of faces.

The party organiser looked aghast.

The children eyed each other gleefully.

So *that* was it! A *magician*! Mystery solved at last.

Something else was very clear to them too. The minister was in Big Trouble!

7. Christmas Greetings

A "Happy Christmas" greeting
From Bill and Barbie Bray
We're sure you're keen to read our news
So here goes – no delay
It's been a year of troubles
The longed-for cruise fell through
We both went down with viruses
Then Bill had full-blown flu
The children keep us busy
(Though adults now, of course)
Rebecca broke an arm and leg
When falling off her horse
Poor Bob's been made redundant
Patricia crashed her car
She'll soon be out of hospital
But all her cuts will scar
Our house was broken into
And struck by lightning too
The damage was extensive and
There's still a lot to do
Old Uncle Ned is failing
He won't be with us long
Bill's sister's had a breakdown
(Well, her nerves were never strong)
Our nephew's been arrested
He's innocent, of course
It's just a little mix-up
In the midst of his divorce
Well, that's our festive update
Enjoy the Christmas cheer
Have fun this special happy time
And through the coming year

8. Christmas Weather

Why does snow always make me feel Christmassy? I've only experienced two or three white Christmases in my whole life, and one of those was freezing fog rather than snow. The freezing fog was magical – a real Winter Wonderland – but treacherous and certainly not fit to be out in. Even though there was something perversely attractive about it when viewed from the comfort and safety of a warm house, it was actually very unpleasant.

My Christmases have tended to be damp and drizzly, if not raining, and mild to the point of mugginess. I don't remember feeling particularly cold on Christmas morning. Neither do I recall many sharp frosts. Most years the skies have been grey and overcast and lacking in sunshine.

So why does snow always make me feel Christmassy? Why doesn't mild, damp, cloudy weather make me feel Christmassy instead?

9. Please Santa

Dear Santa - Please don't think I'm cheeky
Or picky, ungrateful or rude
(And if you go into the kitchen
I'll make sure I leave you some food)

But Santa I've got a big problem
It keeps going round in my head
I just have this horrible feeling
You're planning to bring me a sled

21

The children in stories my gran reads
Get sleds, new and shiny and red
Each story's the same, and it scares me
- Please bring something different instead

They settle to sleep all excited
Just hoping that Santa will call
And bring them a sled, new and shiny
- I don't find that thrilling at all

And when they wake up in the morning
They find at the end of their bed
The present they'd dreamed of and wished for
- A lovely new shiny red sled

I don't *want* a sled. *Please* don't bring one
I like new and shiny and red
And truly I'm not being fussy
But please, Santa, don't bring a sled

I really don't know how I'd use it
I'm not even sure what you do
We never get snow – hardly ever
I don't want one, even brand new

I hope I'm not hurting your feelings
You *can* leave a gift by my bed
I *would* like some presents – but Santa
Please *don't* bring a shiny red sled

10. Other People's Problems

Maisie winced as a sudden outburst of children's laughter reached her from the street. A group of adults walked by, conversing good-humouredly. Maisie grimaced. Why did other people have to sound so pleasant and happy all the time? Why did she never hear people arguing and getting fractious with each other anymore?

She couldn't remember things being like that in the past. It used to be perfectly normal to hear angry voices and violent quarrels, whereas now, just when she so desperately needed to know that other people had problems too, everybody else appeared to be serene and relaxed.

Maisie never felt serene and relaxed anymore. She didn't have good-humoured conversations anymore. So why should other people? Why did she have to be the only one who felt frustrated and disgruntled all the time?

Maisie was acutely aware that for most of her life happy voices had brought her pleasure. They had been a source of joy to her.

Now they offended her. They irritated her. They made her feel left out and isolated. It wasn't that she particularly wanted to hear people bickering and screaming at each other. It was just that – well, it would be reassuring and perversely comforting to witness signs of feuding and dissatisfaction outside her own miserable existence. Over the last couple of years she had become increasingly bitter and resentful of the good relationships and contentment that seemed to be all around her.

Her own life was becoming more and more unpleasant and she harboured no hope that things could improve, and certainly not in the foreseeable future. She was tired. She was so very, very weary. And lonely. And empty. And really quite close to despair. She wasn't sure she even wanted to live anymore.

That wasn't to say she was feeling suicidal. She hadn't given up on life altogether. It was just that -

"Are you going to make that coffee or not?" came an exasperated screech.

"In a minute," growled Maisie.

Why had she ever been foolish enough to open her home to this demanding, ungracious octogenarian?

Because no one else would have her?

Aunt Hilda, like Maisie, was single and childless. It had made sense for the two of them to share a house when Aunt Hilda decided she couldn't manage on her own anymore. All the other relatives had families and numerous commitments. Maisie was the obvious choice. In fact, she had even been naïve enough to imagine it would be fun. She had always got along quite well with Aunt Hilda. They had been good pals while Maisie was growing up.

Of course, that was a long time ago. Maisie was no longer a timid, eager to please child. She was a self-sufficient middle-aged woman with very strong ideas of her own. Aunt Hilda, meanwhile, had evolved from an indulgent, affirming adult into a *self-*indulgent, undermining dependent.

Maisie had spent many happy hours with Aunt Hilda over the years, but she had never *lived* with her before. She received little support from the other relatives. As far as they were concerned, Aunt Hilda was being looked after and therefore wasn't their problem - and Maisie, as a single, childless woman was well overdue a dose of focusing on somebody other than herself for a while anyway.

Aunt Hilda had a wide circle of friends, and appeared to be very popular within that group but, while these acquaintances applauded Maisie's kindness and remarked on how wonderful it must be to share a home with Hilda, they offered no assistance in dealing with the attention-seeking woman. They would visit Aunt Hilda and sympathise with her and joke and reminisce with her and encourage her to talk about herself, but they never lifted any of the weight off Maisie's shoulders.

24

"Where's that coffee?" yelled Aunt Hilda querulously.

"Do it yourself," snapped Maisie, which she knew was ridiculous because she had already made the coffee and was in the process of carrying it through to her aunt.

Maisie had never considered herself an argumentative or bad-tempered person, and yet these days she seemed to be in a permanent state of ill-humour and scratchiness, reacting petulantly to the slightest little thing and generally being impatient and sharp-tongued.

Perhaps this was the real Maisie, she mused as she plonked the coffee mug down.

"About time," grizzled the old woman. "When are you going to put the Christmas tree up?"

"I'm not putting it up," muttered Maisie. "I'm not bothering with Christmas this year."

Aunt Hilda looked disappointed. Good.

Then Maisie felt ashamed of herself. How could she be so mean? She never used to be cold-hearted like that. Or perhaps it was just that her true self had never come out before. After all, she had never had to test her relationship skills much until Aunt Hilda moved in. She had left home at twenty and had spent the whole of her adult life avoiding close relationships as part of a strategy to keep her life simple. As a child she had certainly had plenty of clashes with her brother, but that kind of behaviour was normal between siblings. Surely that in itself didn't make her an argumentative or nasty person.

She had stuck with a job she neither loved nor hated and had been a reliable and conscientious employee. She'd found herself with enough money to live on, plus a bit to spare. Life had been good in its own modest way. How could everything have suddenly turned so sour and ugly when she tried to do the right thing by a needy relative?

Maisie had switched to part-time work in preparation for taking full retirement in a few months' time. This was a decision she had soon been given cause to regret, a new boss having taken over, making sweeping changes. Maisie had grown to hate her job. She no longer enjoyed working. And she no longer enjoyed coming home. Working part-time had made her more available to Aunt Hilda who, in response, had become more and more demanding and dependent

Of course, she had done far too much for Aunt Hilda early on. She realised that now. One of her aunt's adoring friends had even warned her against it.

"Watch her. She'll take advantage," the friend had said. "She's lovely, but she's lazy and self-indulgent. If someone else will do it for her she won't do it herself."

However, Aunt Hilda had been so sweet and innocent – apparently – at the beginning, struggling so bravely to be independent that Maisie hadn't been able to resist the temptation to jump quickly to her aid. By the time she recognised what was happening – that she was making Aunt Hilda completely helpless – it was too late. The pattern had been set. The system was established. If Maisie so much as suggested that her aunt might be able to do something herself she was assaulted by a torrent of histrionics and accusations of cruelty, insensitivity and lack of understanding.

Aunt Hilda's friend had been right about *lazy* and *self-indulgent* though not, in Maisie's view, about *lovely*.

The doorbell rang. Two of Aunt Hilda's friends had turned up for a visit. One of them thrust a bunch of flowers into Maisie's unwilling arms.

"For the invalid," chirped the caller. "Be a dear and put them in water for her. I know she can't manage it herself. Is she in her armchair?"

"Where else would she be?" mumbled Maisie to herself as she flounced to the kitchen. "*Can't manage it herself*! WON'T, more like."

She made as much noise as possible finding a vase and filling it with water. She had no desire to hear Aunt Hilda filling her guests' heads with stories of how ill she was and how difficult life was for her, and laying it on so believably – as she always did - that she could win an award for her acting.

Maisie had learned early on in their house-sharing that if she joined in any conversation involving Aunt Hilda and visitors she would spend the whole time either contradicting her aunt or trying to bite her tongue. Whichever way it went, she would get agitated and show herself in a bad light, while Aunt Hilda would lap up sympathy and admiration for how courageously she coped.

It was impossible to shut out Aunt Hilda's monologue completely.

"Maisie's absolutely wonderful," sang a treacly stoical voice. "I don't know *what* I'd do without her. I must be a terrible drain on her. I'm such a poor, decrepit old thing. I would never have moved in with her if I'd known how quickly I would deteriorate and become a burden on her. I'm such a nuisance."

That was another of Aunt Hilda's ploys. Pre-emptive, self-effacing gratitude, which invariably resulted in an outpouring of compassion and reassurance.

"Of course you're no trouble to her," said one voice. "You can't help being disabled. And you're in so much pain. Don't be so hard on yourself."

"I'm sure you give far more than you take," added the other. "And she's only got herself to worry about. It's not as if she's got any family of her own making demands on her. It isn't much to ask of her to give a bit of attention to an aunt who's done so much for *her* over the years. She's lucky to have you."

Aunt Hilda sighed bravely.

"That's very kind of you," she wavered. "She's in such good health herself that she has no idea what it feels like to be old and tired and struggling to keep going."

Maisie poked her head round the living-room door.

27

"I'm going to buy some fairy lights," she said gruffly.

"I thought you weren't going to bother with Christmas," called Aunt Hilda in that taunting tone that made Maisie want to throw something at her.

Maisie grabbed her purse, shopping bag and coat and stomped out of the house to the sound of, "She's over-tired, poor lamb. Doesn't know what she's saying half the time."

Maisie *wasn't* going to bother with Christmas, but she needed to get out of the house – preferably before Aunt Hilda thought of offering her guests coffee - and buying fairy lights was the first excuse that came to mind.

The idea hadn't come entirely out of the blue. Maisie loved fairy lights and really didn't want to miss out on them just because she was punishing Aunt Hilda. Her old fairy lights had been very temperamental the year before and Maisie had been planning to purchase some new ones secretly anyway. She would drape them in her bedroom and be completely selfish and have them all to herself and not share them with her miserable, cantankerous, ungrateful aunt at all.

As she approached the bus stop she was greeted by a beaming, vaguely familiar face.

"How's your aunt?" asked the lady with cheerful solicitude. "I haven't seen her for ages."

Maisie felt her hackles rise. Was there *no* escape from Aunt Hilda?

"She's fine," replied Maisie curtly. "Doesn't get out much at the moment."

The lady sighed sadly.

"Oh, that's such a shame," she said. "She's such a lovely person. It must be so frustrating for her."

"She's all right," muttered Maisie.

"Well, I saw Bea the other day," chipped in another lady, "and she'd been to visit Hilda and was very concerned about her. Said she looked dreadful, and in so much pain she couldn't move. Bea told Hilda she ought to get the doctor, but Hilda refused because she didn't want to be a nuisance."

The speaker turned to Maisie.

"You really ought to insist your aunt see a doctor," she implored. "Don't let her bravery fool you. She's in a very bad way."

Maisie forced herself to smile.

"I'll have a word with her," she mumbled.

The bus arrived. Maisie settled as far away from her aunt's fan club as possible.

She sat on her own, fuming at the recollection of all those false claims about Aunt Hilda. Apart from the fact that Aunt Hilda *wasn't* a lovely person, she most certainly wasn't in too much pain to move. She could jump up easily and quickly enough if she wanted the TV remote control and Maisie was out of sight and didn't respond to the summons.

And Aunt Hilda most definitely didn't have any qualms about being a nuisance. In fact she *loved* medical attention, which was partly - Maisie suspected - why she invented so many ailments. She never look ill to Maisie, except when she was doing her "dying duck" act which, admittedly, she did very convincingly. She could produce the weak voice, drawn face and languid demeanour at the drop of a hat, and shake them off just as readily.

"Well, it's going to be his last Christmas," came an unknown female voice behind her. "He's failing fast now. But we'll make the best of it. He's had a long, hard struggle and it's been heart-breaking to watch ..."

Maisie moved to a different seat. She had no desire to hear about other people's problems. She had enough problems of her own.

"But of course, when her son just dropped dead like that, for no apparent reason..."

"Still it puts your own troubles into perspective, doesn't it?" came another voice. "My house burning down is nothing compared with that."

Maisie sighed. *That seat was no good either.* She didn't want to hear about people dropping dead without warning or having their homes burnt down. She tried a third seat.

"Of course, he's never been the same since he reacted badly to that mistake they made with his medication," – a male voice this time. "Did permanent damage, they reckon. It's awful for his family. They can't do anything the way they used to. And he can't be left on his own, so that means they can never all go out at the same time."

"Well, that's how it got with my wife, you see, among other things" responded the unseen companion. "A rare form of degenerative brain disease. Really bad. She had to go into a home in the end. Broke my heart and I felt awful, like I'd abandoned her. But, honestly, I just couldn't cope anymore. I'm on my way to visit her now and wish her a Happy Christmas. Not that she'll know what I'm on about. This is my stop coming up now. See you, mate."

The two men wished each other Merry Christmas and then the one with the wife in a home staggered to the front of the bus and alighted. Maisie felt furious with them. *Merry Christmas*! she thought angrily. How could they have the nerve to talk about a *Merry Christmas* when they'd just been discussing such tragedy? Everyone on the bus seemed to be competing for tales of tragedy and suffering. Wasn't *anyone* all right?

Uninvited, the words of an earlier overheard conversation floated into her mind. *Still it puts your own troubles into perspective, doesn't it?*

Maisie tried to contradict the statement in the privacy of her own thoughts, but she couldn't. It was true. There was no getting away from it. Everyone had problems – well nearly everyone anyway.

But not everyone was bitter and twisted about it, Maisie reflected grudgingly. Other people coped with their problems. Other people kept things in perspective and still appreciated what was good in their lives. Other people stayed amiable and cheerful, regardless of what was going on behind the scenes.

Christmas is about love and goodwill, Maisie reminded herself. *And peace,* of course.

Without love, peace and goodwill life was pretty grim, as Maisie had discovered to her cost. Dispensing with love, peace and goodwill caused nothing but misery. Since Maisie had become bitter and twisted she had been desperately unhappy and, in return, had behaved more and more irritably and uncharitably towards Aunt Hilda.

Yes, Aunt Hilda was a pain in the neck and a terrible trial, but did that mean Maisie had to repay her in kind? Did Aunt Hilda deserve to be treated harshly just because she was cantankerous and disagreeable?

Maisie had compromised her own standards of behaviour and her own sense of self-worth by retaliating increasingly petulantly to Aunt Hilda's provocation. She didn't know herself or trust herself anymore and she hated that. Being crabby and argumentative achieved nothing positive and made her feel bad about herself.

There was nothing else for it. She would have to give love and goodwill another chance – and peace, of course. It wouldn't be easy. Aunt Hilda tried her patience and goodwill to its limits, but she *must* give it another go. She *must* learn to rise above her frustrations and hurt feelings. It wouldn't be easy, but she must make a concerted effort to do it.

Maisie bought *three* sets of fairy lights. One for *her* bedroom. One for Aunt Hilda's bedroom. And one for the Christmas tree – which she *would* put up.

11. A Festival Of Christmas Trees

A weekend of brightness and beauty
Of fellowship, joy and goodwill
Excitement and wide-eyed enchantment
A scene to delight and to thrill

An atmosphere bustling and happy
A colourful, sparkling display
Of trees with their own special message
A masterpiece, each, in its way

To add to the fun, slips for voting
- A task causing anguish untold
For how can *the best* be selected
When *all* are a joy to behold?

Tombola with *all* winning numbers
A gift stall with goodies galore
Games, prizes - guess name, weight, find treasure
Refreshments too. Who could ask more?

Then worship on Sunday, quite novel
With seats placed in spaces round trees
Inspiring, a time to feel thankful
Though best not to fidget or sneeze!

A weekend of fun and contentment
A triumph! A total success
Well worth all the hard work and effort?
The planning and weariness? ... *Yes!*

12. Nine Across

"Okay. Nine across," Mal said to himself. "*The number of Wise Men who visited Jesus.* Seven letters."

Well, that was easy. *Three.*

Hang on! *Three* had five letters, not seven. The seven must be a misprint.

Mal checked the grid and, to his amazement, discovered that there really were seven letters in the answer. How could that be? Everyone knew it was three Wise Men who visited Jesus.

Ah well, he would leave that for now and come back to it later.

He worked his way through the remaining Across clues of his Bumper Christmas Crossword and solved them without too much difficulty. Then he started on the Down clues and, after filling in the first few answers, suddenly realised that he had put in the last letter of Nine Across without even noticing. That should help. And it was definitely right.

Away in a - , popular carol, six letters. That had to be *Manger*, no two ways about it. *Away in a Manger*. Manger gave him an *n* at the end of Nine Across.

Seven letters, ending in *n*. How could that be *three*? It *couldn't* be three. Had they printed the wrong clue? It was bad if they had. It was like giving someone a jigsaw puzzle with a piece missing. They should have been more careful. It wasn't fair to disappoint people like that.

Had they really messed up? Or were they just being sneaky? Was there a fancy word for *three*, perhaps?

Threesome? No. Too long and it ended in *e*.

Triune? Was that a word? Too short anyway, and the wrong last letter.

Trinity? That was a good religious sounding word.

Mal felt excited. It had seven letters as well. He started writing it in and then stopped abruptly. It ended in *y*, not *n*. He sighed and erased it. Good job he was using pencil and not ink.

Triumvirate? Too long. Wrong last letter.

Triangle? Don't be silly.

Was it an actual number, he wondered, but not *three*? That would be cheating on the part of the compilers, but it was worth considering. *Anything* was worth considering.

Were there any numbers with seven letters, ending in *n*?

Fifteen … Sixteen … He had never heard of fifteen or sixteen Wise Men. There were only three. They brought gold, frankincense and myrrh. Everybody knew that. There were THREE.

It didn't make sense. He would come back to it later. There were still two more letters he could put in to help him – if only he could solve *those* clues! He would keep *fifteen* and *sixteen* in mind, just in case there had been several extra Wise Men hanging around that he didn't know about. He could get the second letter and the fifth letter of Nine Across from Down answers and then he would find out whether it was *fifteen* or *sixteen*.

The second and fifth letters of *fifteen* and *sixteen* were the same. Aargh!

Umpteen! That might be it. It had the right number of letters and it ended in *n*. And, more to the point, it had different second and fifth letters from *fifteen* and *sixteen*. Worth remembering.

"Have you set that table yet?" came Anika's voice from the kitchen. "Dinner's nearly ready."

"Just about to do it," lied Mal. "Ani! How many Wise Men were there?"

"Wise Men?" asked Anika, poking a puzzled head round the door. "Oh, you mean the three kings?"

"Yes," prompted Mal. "How many were there?"

Anika gaped and then chortled.

"Three, of course," she spluttered. "Come on. Get that table set."

She returned to the kitchen, chuckling to herself.

After dinner Mal attacked his crossword with renewed vigour. He had had an inspiration during the meal and was impatient to follow through on it.

What if Nine Across wasn't anything to do with the number three? What if it was a collective noun, like a herd of cattle or a flock of sheep? Perhaps there was a special word for a group of wise men or kings. Hopefully it wasn't anything too obscure because that wouldn't be fair.

Then it came to him. *Caravan*! He was sure *caravan* could be used to refer to a group of people travelling across the desert, and the Wise Men came on *camels*!

Caravan had seven letters and ended in *n*! He'd got it! He'd solved it at last! He was about to scribble it in when he remembered his earlier mistake with *Trinity* and restrained himself. He'd better check the Down clues for the second and fifth letters before committing himself.

"*Struggles with chimneys?* Five letters," Mal read slowly, not for the first time. The clue was posed as a question, suggesting it was some kind of trick. "*Sweep*, maybe? Sweep's got five letters."

But what did chimney sweeps have to do with Christmas, even allowing for some kind of clever twist? And *sweep* would give him *e* as the second letter, which didn't work for *caravan* anyway. So it couldn't be *sweep*.

He moved on to the fifth letter. That needed to be a *v*, which would narrow down the options nicely.

Prickly decoration. Five letters.

Ivy!

No. Not enough letters. And ivy wasn't prickly anyway. Holly was the prickly one. *Holly*? That was a sensible answer, but *holly* would give him an *o*, not a *v*, which would rule out *caravan*.

Aargh!

Platoon! ... *Dragoon*! ... *Festoon*!

Was *festoon* a collective term? He couldn't recall what it meant offhand, but it would fit with the *e* of *sweep*, so maybe he'd cracked it at last.

"Ani!" he bellowed eagerly, "What's *festoon* a group of?"

"You what?" exclaimed Anika, stomping into the room, brandishing a soggy tea towel.

"Is *festoon* one of those collective words for a group of something?" Mal clarified.

Anika hooted. She laughed and laughed and laughed until there were tears rolling down her cheeks and she could hardly hold herself upright.

"No, you ninny," she guffawed. "Festoon is what you do with your decorations when you hang them up."

Mal felt foolish and humiliated. Why had he opened his big mouth?

Anika ruffled his hair affectionately.

"I think you need a break from that silly crossword torture," she said more gently. "The sink's blocked again. Come on. Help me fix it."

Mal followed her meekly to the kitchen, still contemplating his three Wise Men.

Festoon was a Christmas word, even if it wasn't a collective noun, so –

"Plunger," ordered Anika.

"What?"

"Plunger," Anika repeated. "Pass me the plunger, please."

He handed her the plunger.

Could *festoon* still be linked with the three Wise Men in some way? He really needed that second letter to confirm the *e*.

Was there anything Christmassy associated with chimneys? Well, Father Christmas and the reindeer, of course, but they didn't fit the letters. *Sleigh*! No. Too many letters.

Aargh!

"Come on, dreamy," teased Anika. "Help me with this sink or Santa won't bring you any presents."

Santa! Five letters. Struggles with chimneys! That was it! *Santa*!

So *Santa* would give him another *n*. Something *n*, something, something *o* – he was certain *holly* was right – something *n*.

Whatever could it be?

Mal worked on his crossword for the rest of the evening – when Anika would allow it, that was – and by bedtime had finished it. Apart from Nine Across.

He had enjoyed tackling his Bumper Christmas Crossword. It had taken a huge amount of effort and painful brain work, to say nothing of time, but he had triumphed and he felt good about it.

Well, he had *almost* triumphed. That was the problem. Nine across still eluded him. And the infuriating thing was it just didn't make sense.

"Nine across" Mal recited as he settled down in bed. "*The number of Wise Men who visited Jesus.* Seven letters. Something *n*, something, something *o*, something *n*."

Aargh! He would never sleep.

A few minutes later he was snoring.

Next day, which was Saturday, Anika sent him out for some groceries. As he sauntered home he spotted a group of people coming out of church. That was weird. It wasn't even a Sunday. One of the ladies had a dog collar on, so she was obviously a vicar or something.

Dare he ask her about the Wise Men?

Why not? He had nothing to lose.

Well – she might try and convert him, but he could always run away if necessary.

Mal took a deep breath and approached the crowd of churchgoers before he could lose his nerve.

"Excuse me. How many Wise Men visited Jesus?" he enquired politely, addressing the lady in the dog collar.

"Good question," she replied cheerfully.

That was a surprise.

"We tend to assume there were three," continued the clergy person, "because they brought three gifts -"

"Gold, frankincense and myrrh," chipped in Mal proudly.

"That's right," agreed the clergy person warmly. Mal liked her. There was nothing stuffy or self-righteous about her. "But the Bible doesn't actually say how many wise men there were. It just says that certain wise men from the east came to pay homage to Jesus. The specific number is unknown. There *might* have been three. Or there might have been thirteen - or thirty - or three hundred."

"Or three thousand," offered one of her companions brightly.

Mal was amazed.

"Well, well," he responded, shaking his head. "I never knew that."

"Not many people do," the clergy person assured him with that kind, gentle smile. "In fact there's a lot we don't know about the Christmas story, and most of what we *think* we know isn't mentioned in the Bible at all."

She stopped talking to jot down some Bible references for Mal.

"If you'd like to check it out this is where you'll find the Christmas story," she told him, handing him a piece of paper. "I can let you have a Bible if you need one."

"No, I'm okay, thanks," garbled Mal, squirming uncomfortably.

Was this the part where she started converting him?

"That's fine," chirped the clergy person. "Christmas blessings."

Mal went on his way, relieved at having escaped, and feeling almost heroic.

He chewed over his new understanding of the strange crossword clue. So the number of Wise Men was unknown. He needed to come up with a word for unknown that had seven letters, ending in *n*, with second letter *n* and fifth letter *o*.

What could it be? He racked his brain all the way home.

As soon as he got in he grabbed his crossword and stared eagerly at the empty spaces.

"Aren't you going to put the shopping away?" Anika challenged him irritably, hands on hips. "Do I have to do *everything* myself?"

Distractedly, Mal unpacked the shopping.

"Unknown," he said to himself. "A word for unknown – something *n*, something, something *o*, something *n*."

Unknown ... unknown ... unknown ... He couldn't think of any other words for unknown.

Hang on! He almost dropped a box of eggs. *UNKNOWN* had seven letters! *UNKNOWN* was something *n*, something, something *o*, something *n*!

The answer was *UNKNOWN*! The number of Wise Men who visited Jesus was *unknown*!

He'd done it! At last! He'd actually done it! Phew!

And he'd learned something too. He couldn't wait to air his knowledge about the three kings! He would get as much mileage out of it as possible.

13. Time To Reflect

A time for reflection,
For calm contemplation
A time for thanksgiving and prayer
A time for reviewing
Perhaps for renewing
A time to take stock and prepare

But life gets so busy
It isn't that easy
To slow down, relax and be still
To question and wonder
Consider and ponder
The role of love, peace and goodwill

And yet I must do it
Must guide myself through it
I must make the effort and try
To probe how I'm feeling
And find inner healing
To know what I'm seeking and why

14. Getting It Right

Every Christmas I vow to get it right.

I will NOT get bogged down with practicalities and lose sight of its real meaning. I will NOT get fretful when things go wrong. I will NOT make Christmas all about me and how I feel and what I want.

I will make time during Advent to prepare properly, spiritually. I will soak up the thrill of the season and wake up on Christmas morning with a true sense of joy and wonder.

Yet every Christmas I get it wrong. I focus on the practicalities to the exclusion of anything spiritual. To my intense frustration and disappointment, I never seem to feel quite ready for the Carol Service, an important event in my anticipation of Christmas. I overreact to the slightest hiccup, declaring melodramatically that "Christmas is ruined". Even if I manage to keep a few days clear for calm reflection something will invariably crop up that demands my full attention or drains me emotionally. So still I fail to tune myself in properly to Christmas.

Life has taught me that if I don't feel "Christmassy" in the lead-up to Christmas I won't suddenly feel "Christmassy" when the day arrives either, and my longing to relax and enjoy the Twelve Days of Christmas will not be fulfilled.

It's easy to blame external forces and pressures for my difficulty in tuning into Christmas, but I know the problem is within me. I don't prepare properly and then I miss Christmas. I observe it, but I don't experience it, and then I feel empty and cheated.

I long so desperately to get it right and yet, year after year, I get it wrong.

Will I ever get it right?

15. The Finishing Touch

The tree was exquisite, delightful
- Though modesty didn't allow
An open display of self-praising
She took a deep breath and sighed, "WOW!"

The fairy lights, vivid and cheerful
Were draped with precision and flair
The baubles, so shiny and vibrant
She'd placed with meticulous care

Her tinsel was tastefully languid
- Untidily graceful by choice -
The total effect was amazing
She just couldn't help but rejoice

And now the *Pièce de Résistance*
Her glorious finishing touch
The new star, a golden sensation
- No wonder it cost her so much

The old star was flimsy and bendy
And always looked ready to drop
But *this* star was sturdy and solid
No danger that *this* one would flop

This new star was fit for a palace
It glittered and glistened and gleamed
It captured the light with each twinkle
She'd purchased perfection, it seemed

She climbed on a chair to install it
Then stood back and gazed in pure bliss
She'd never seen anything like it
And *she* was creator of this!

But – horror! The tree started tilting
The star was too heavy, it found
She froze as it tipped in slow motion
Then suddenly crashed to the ground

16. The Soirée

"His wife should have known better," grumbled Jane. "What was she thinking, agreeing to a party – or *soirée*, as he insists on calling it – on the twenty-second of December? Hasn't she got anything better to do with her evenings this close to Christmas? It'll serve her right if she isn't ready in time."

Martin smiled ruefully.

"Perhaps she's more organised than we are," he threw out hesitantly, and then winced as Jane's eyes flared with anger.

Her fury rendered her speechless for a moment and, to Martin's relief, she made an effort to compose herself before responding verbally.

"Oh, of course, she's *perfect*," growled Jane, folding her arms sulkily.

It was a much milder retort than Martin had expected.

"That's unfair," he chided his wife calmly. "We don't know anything about Mrs. Hayden, except that she's supporting her husband – hopefully graciously - in something he has chosen to do. Whether they made the decision together or whether he just inflicted it on her is not for us to know."

Jane unfolded her arms and then folded them again.

"Well, they could have at least invited the whole family so that we wouldn't have to find babysitters," she muttered.

"It's a special *Thank You* to his group of helpers," explained Martin wearily. "Not a big party. I don't understand why you're being so grumpy about it."

"No, you don't understand," mumbled Jane. "That's the problem."

Martin didn't understand anything about being a vicar's wife because he wasn't a vicar's wife. He was "the vicar". He was the important one. He had no concept of what it was like to do everything as "the vicar's wife" … to go everywhere – regardless of whether she wanted to go or not - as "the vicar's wife" … to be an accessory rather than a person in her own right …

To be fair, she mostly enjoyed being a vicar's wife and embraced the challenges gladly, but somehow this Christmas things had been crowding in on her. There seemed to be so many extra demands on her – because she was "the vicar's wife" – and so little time or energy left for her own Christmas arrangements and family concerns. She had been criticised – because she was "the vicar's wife" – for things going wrong that weren't even anything to do with her. She was fed up. And she wanted an evening at home.

Jane realised Martin was waiting for her to elaborate on her statement.

"I'm being grumpy because I've got to go to some party I don't want to go to, just because I'm your wife," she snapped. "Not because anyone wants *me* for *me*."

"That's not true," Martin contradicted her comfortingly. "We're *both* in David's group of helpers."

"I'm only in the group because I'm 'the vicar's wife'," Jane threw back, flouncing out of the room to greet the babysitter.

David Hayden was head of the town's Church of England Primary School and had been keen for Martin and Jane, as local vicar and wife, to become active members of the team responsible for the religious life of the school.

The team comprised two teachers, two mothers of pupils at the school, David Hayden, and Martin and Jane. Collectively they were nicknamed the God Squad. Mrs. Hayden, to Jane's knowledge, had no direct dealings with the school and, as Martin had stated, was an unknown quantity.

The two mums were a fascinating combination. They appeared to be firm friends, despite their different temperaments and attitudes. Charlotte was assertive and opinionated, though not unlikeable with it. Olivia, the quieter one, came across as rather earnest and intense.

The teachers had contrasting personalities too, Kerry being bubbly, vivacious and fun-loving, while Viv was staid and had a tendency to brusqueness. Viv was unashamedly old-fashioned and authoritarian. Children needed discipline, she averred. Children needed clearly defined boundaries and rules. Children needed controlling, not just to keep them civilised, but to keep them happy as well. She made no apology for laying it on heavily at school because, as she saw it, most children got precious little of it anywhere else.

Viv struck Jane as something of a Jeckyll and Hyde character. It was very noticeable that when there were no children around to witness her softer side, Viv invariably morphed into a friendly, good-humoured and benevolent human being.

There were several cars already there when they arrived at the Haydens' house, and Martin and Jane struggled to find a place to park.

"How inconsiderate taking up all that space!" raged Jane. "I bet we're the last to arrive."

"Probably," agreed Martin grimly.

He resisted the temptation to ask Jane whose fault it was that they were late.

David Hayden let them in. His greeting was friendly but formal. It was clearly not going to be a very relaxed evening. On the surface everything would be polite and congenial, but beneath the festive exterior people would be feeling uneasy and scared of doing or saying something wrong.

As she crossed the threshold into the house Jane experienced an unexpected and not altogether welcome sensation of being soothed and comforted. There was an air of warmth, calm and happiness – contentment – that disarmed her for a moment. This was a home full of love and – yes, kindness. Jane tried to brush the idea aside. How could she possibly learn so much about a home she had never visited before just by taking a few steps into the hall? It was ridiculous. Nonsense.

Yet she couldn't shake off that disconcerting feeling of serenity.

A tantalising baking aroma wafted towards them. Jane tried to ignore the thrill it gave her.

"Something smells good," said Martin, sniffing approvingly.

"Hannah's warming up the mince pies," David explained.

David ushered them into the living-room. Jane was enchanted, in spite of herself. Dainty fairy lights were strewn around, twinkling prettily. The small tree was modestly but attractively decorated. Not too plain. Not too fancy. Just right. On a cupboard close to the tree there was a neat little nativity scene.

Carols were playing softly in the background and Jane noted, with grudging pleasure, that the singing was brisk and traditional in style – just as she would have chosen for herself - rather than sentimental or like a pop song.

The whole environment was tasteful and unassuming.

A petite woman scurried into the room and apologised for her negligence. David introduced her as his wife Hannah.

Mrs. Hayden smiled radiantly. Her whole face smiled, not just her mouth. She smiled from within. It was a genuinely warm, friendly smile. There was nothing artificial or forced about it. Jane was annoyed to discover that she felt at ease.

Mrs. Hayden's face was pleasant, though not pretty by any means. In fact she was quite plain really. It was only that engaging smile that made her look reasonably attractive. Jane conceded reluctantly that Mrs. Hayden displayed no airs or graces at all. She appeared unsophisticated and ingenuous. Jane would have preferred Mrs. Hayden to be snobby and supercilious, thereby justifying her determined animosity.

Jane recognised everyone else. Viv and Kerry, the teachers, were there, as were mums Charlotte and Olivia. Hannah Hayden was the only one not in the "God Squad". She was the only one who had no connection or involvement with the school in her own right. Jane wondered how many of her guests Mrs. Hayden actually knew. Had she met them all in another context? Maybe she was familiar with the teachers, Viv and Kerry, but probably not with the mums, and certainly not with Jane or Martin.

"Shall I fetch the coffee and mince pies?" Mrs. Hayden asked her husband.

He nodded.

She checked how many teas and coffees were required and then rushed off to the kitchen, hotly pursued by Viv and Kerry, which led Jane to conclude that Mrs. Hayden did indeed already know the two teachers.

The three women returned a few minutes later, Mrs. Hayden carrying a plate of mince pies, and Viv and Kerry wielding trays of cups and saucers (*not mugs,* Jane observed with wry satisfaction).

"Careful not to burn yourselves on the mince pies," Mrs. Hayden warned everyone cheerfully as she offered the plate around. "I think I left them in a bit too long."

"All this wonderful home baking, Hannah," Charlotte congratulated her, indicating a display of goodies on a low table in the centre of the room. "Chocolate cake. Coffee cake. Shortbread. Mince pies. You've been busy."

"I've been baking all week," laughed Hannah in response. "I'm worn out!"

Probably got nothing else to do, thought Jane sourly. *Has she even got any children to look after and take up her time and energy?*

Jane had been studying the room. It was all very nice and, to be fair, cosy and homely, despite not having a thing out of place. But there were no toys. There were no photos of children. There were no children's Christmas pictures. There was no sign of children, or teenagers, at all.

The Haydens were in their thirties. Or maybe their early forties? Certainly no older, and certainly young enough to have their family still at home. Yet there was no sign – or sound - of any children. Even if the Haydens' offspring been bundled off to bed early, surely there would be thuds from above. Surely there would be *something* to hint at their presence or existence.

Jane snorted to herself. They probably didn't *want* children. Hannah – no, *Mrs. Hayden*. Jane had no desire to be on first-name terms with this "perfect" woman – probably didn't want to risk ruining her trim little figure.

Or perhaps she *couldn't* have children. The possibility came unbidden into Jane's mind. Perhaps the Haydens wanted children but couldn't have any.

Jane dismissed the thought angrily. She was in no mood to feel sympathy for people she resented.

Having finished handing round the mince pies, Mrs. Hayden reached across the table to deposit her empty plate in a space, moving the sugar bowl to one side as she did so. Her hand caught the end of the teaspoon. The spoon flipped dramatically and scattered sugar over the table and on to the floor. Hannah let out an anguished cry and her eyes filled with tears. Within a split second she had composed herself, and Jane suspected that most people hadn't even witnessed her fleeting discomfiture, but it had happened none-the-less.

Kerry made a light-hearted quip about throwing food around, to which there was no response, but other than that the incident passed without comment. Jane noticed that David was watching his wife solicitously, his eyes calling out to her in comfort. Hannah glanced at him fleetingly and seemed to catch the look. In that brief moment they exchanged tender smiles, and Jane felt certain Hannah's distress had not been caused by fear of an overbearing, demanding husband.

David and Hannah really did seem to be a genuinely devoted couple. Maybe Hannah had just put too much pressure on herself to get everything right. She was human. She was vulnerable. Jane felt a rush of compassion and empathy for her and tried to shake it off, but couldn't.

She realised, with a confusing mixture of relief and irritation, that she didn't want to shake it off. She *liked* Hannah. She had grown quite fond of her in the short time she had been in her home.

It struck Jane suddenly that behind the sunny smile and warm demeanour Hannah Hayden looked tired and drawn. The happiness was genuine, Jane felt certain, but this gentle little soul was clearly under some kind of strain, or at least was not as laid back as she appeared.

"Tell us one of your *Dark, Dark Tales*, Viv!" urged Kerry suddenly.

Kerry beamed round at the group.

"They're hilarious. Trust me," she trilled. "She makes them up as she goes along."

Viv looked doubtful, yet enthusiastic at the same time.

"Well, if everyone wants me to," she offered, eagerness oozing out of every pore.

Jane, still attempting to hold on to her anger, resolved not to be amused. However, in no time at all, she found herself laughing so much there were tears rolling down her cheeks. Her face ached. She couldn't remember the last time she had heard anything as funny as Viv's spoof horror story.

Then David announced, with a wicked grin, that he was going to test their brain power. Jane glared at her husband, willing him to check his watch and declare that it was time to go home. She *hated* being put on the spot.

"It's just a seasonal quiz," said Hannah encouragingly, catching Jane's eye. "Just for the group. Not individually. Nothing to embarrass anyone."

The quiz was great fun. Jane thoroughly enjoyed herself, and all the more so because she discovered that her general knowledge appeared to be better than most of her companions'. Of course, it was impossible to judge how many answers David knew as he was in charge of the questions. Kerry teased him mercilessly about hiding his ignorance behind being the "expert" testing everybody else. He took it all in good part.

Jane wondered what kind of boss he was. He had a reputation for running a tight ship, and had always struck her as aloof and rather uptight at their "God Squad" meetings. He had certainly never come across as someone who would share a joke with his staff. Perhaps Kerry understood him well enough to know how far, and in what circumstances, she could push him.

Or would she suffer when school returned? Somehow Jane doubted it. This was a party. Everyone was relaxed and happy and full of Christmas goodwill. Even David. Even Jane herself. Though it grieved her to admit it, it was shaping up to be one of the best get-togethers she had ever been to.

They munched their way through gluttonous amounts of cake and shortbread, and had their cups refilled as many times as they desired. Jane settled for just one cup of coffee and was astonished when Charlotte requested a *third* cup of tea.

They chattered exuberantly, and reminisced joyfully and shared jokes and anecdotes.

"Keep them clean," David admonished his guests when the jokes began.

Kerry's contribution came dangerously close to *not* being clean.

David gave her a stern look.

"That's as low as the tone gets," he chided her, but with a twinkle in his eye.

Hannah brought out a dish of homemade chocolate truffles.

"Oh! These are to *die* for!" exclaimed Kerry, closing her eyes in delight as she bit into hers.

There were grunts of agreement, although David declared that he wouldn't go *that* far.

"Are they difficult to make?" enquired Olivia.

"Not really," replied Hannah. "They make your arms ache though."

Charlotte asked for the recipe.

"They're *very very* naughty," confessed Hannah, diving into a cupboard and fishing out a notepad. "And *very very* extravagant."

She tore off sheets of paper for all those who wanted to write down the recipe.

"I first learned to make these when I was about seven," Hannah told the group brightly. "And I just couldn't believe I had created something so delicious. Are you ready? Okay, so it's four heaped tablespoons of icing sugar. Eight heaped tablespoons of drinking chocolate - "

"*Eight*?" screeched Charlotte.

"Yes, eight," chuckled Hannah. "I told you it was extravagant! Mix with four ounces of butter. Roll into balls and cover with hundreds and thousands or chocolate strands."

All voices fell silent for a moment while people scribbled down the details.

"I'm going to make some tomorrow!" proclaimed Jane eagerly.

"So am I," chimed in Charlotte.

"I always store them in the fridge," concluded Hannah. "But I think they're nicer to eat if you thaw them out a bit beforehand."

The cheery chatter resumed. Time flew by. Jane was amazed when she glanced surreptitiously at her watch.

"It's nearly ten past ten!" she cried.

"Oh dear, we've imposed on you for too long," gasped Olivia, looking apologetically at David and Hannah, who were sitting together.

David waved a dismissive hand.

"Nonsense. *You* haven't imposed on *us*," he assured his guests. "But we've probably kept you away from home for longer than we should have done."

Hannah jumped up.

"Don't go for a minute," she urged them.

She dashed out of the room and reappeared a few seconds later carrying – precariously – a large box.

David leapt to her assistance and relieved her of her burden.

"A little something for you to take home," Hannah explained, lifting out gift bags and handing them round.

"Oh, you shouldn't have," protested Viv.

"She wanted to," asserted David with an indulgent smile. "Don't worry. It's just a few novelties. Nothing much."

"Are they all the same?" asked Kerry, easing open her bag and peering inside.

"No," replied Hannah. "They're similar kinds of things, but they're all slightly different."

"Good," said Kerry. "In that case I can open mine without spoiling anyone else's surprise."

Jane watched in delight as Kerry fished out a notebook, a pen, a tape measure, a duster, a comb, a small bar of chocolate, a coaster with a robin on it, a ball of string and a variety pack box of cereal.

Jane decided to save her gift bag for Christmas Day.

She just had one problem as she and Martin made their way home. Should she - would she ever be able to - admit to him that it had been a wonderful evening and she was really glad he had pressured her into going?

17. A Gift For Two

A gift for him, a gift for her
But what would be the best?
… A loving couple, newly wed …
- So something for the nest?

A useful thing? A pretty thing?
Cute? Sensible? Or fun?
A gift to share? Yes, *that* seems right
- But simpler said than done

A gift for both, but split in two
Each piece with vital role
Unworkable alone but put
Together, perfect! Whole! …

They're keen on nuts … now *there's* a thought
A special Christmas treat
- Some nuts with shells that must be cracked
To make them fit to eat!

Yes, nuts for him, the tool for her
Together they can crack
Together they can share the fun
And munch their Christmas snack

18. Childhood Christmas

Remember the thrill and excitement?
That endless wait, eagerly borne
For Christmas Eve, Santa and presents
That longing to wake and it's morn?

Remember the magical feeling
Just knowing that Santa had been?
That longed-for assortment of parcels
With fine gifts inside, yet unseen?

Remember the tears and frustration?
- That day was so special and yet
Intense, overwhelming and tiring
So happy - and then so upset

Remember the thrill and excitement?
It's come at last! Christmas is here!
And when it was over, the anguish?
I can't wait another whole year!

19. Something Special For Grandpa

"He asked me the same question four times in about ten minutes," said Josh mournfully. "It was awful. I didn't know what to do. I just kept answering him as if it was the first time he'd asked."

Grandpa had been diagnosed with dementia and fourteen-year-old Josh was struggling to cope with the idea. His sister, two years his senior, was more philosophical about it.

"That's the best way to deal with it," Lauren assured him. "There's no point in getting upset about it. Just go with the flow. He's okay."

"No, he *isn't* okay," Josh contradicted emotionally. "He's got dementia. He'll never be okay again."

"But he's still Grandpa," Lauren insisted. "He's still the same person inside. He's still got his feelings. He's still got his sense of humour. He's still got his memories, and they're very much a part of him. He's clear about the past. It's just the here and now he has trouble sorting out. Encourage him to reminisce about his childhood. He gets really animated then. He's still Grandpa, Josh, and the dementia's in its early stages. He's a long way off not knowing who we are. And we can still have a decent conversation with him. It just isn't quite as straightforward as it used to be."

Lauren chucked Josh under the chin, like she used to when he was little. He nearly smiled. She did it again and that time he did smile.

"He's coming for Christmas," Lauren concluded. "We'll make it as special as we can for him. Let's try and think of all the things he's enjoyed about Christmas over the years. He'll probably still enjoy them even if he can't remember some of them. And we can make sure he gets plenty of all the things he likes best."

They decided to visit Grandpa together after school the following day and get him chatting about Christmas. Then they could work out how to make it extra special for him.

As soon as they arrived, Lauren sent Josh to the kitchen to put the kettle on.

"Would you like tea of coffee, Grandpa?" she asked brightly.

Grandpa looked flustered, as if he didn't understand the question. Josh had stopped abruptly and was staring at Grandpa in dismay. Lauren waved him to the kitchen, but he was rooted to the spot. She reworded her question.

"Would you like a cup of tea, Grandpa?"

Grandpa's face lit up.

"Oh, yes please," he said eagerly. "And there's a packet of chocolate chip cookies in the cupboard. Bring them too."

Lauren gave Josh a reassuring smile.

"I think options confuse him," she whispered. "We need to keep it clear and simple."

Josh nodded and disappeared in the direction of the kitchen.

Soon the three of them were sitting comfortably together drinking tea and munching cookies.

"Looking forward to Christmas, Grandpa?" threw out Lauren clumsily.

Grandpa looked surprised.

"Is it Christmas again already?" he replied. "Why have you got your school uniforms on then?"

"We don't break up for a few days," explained Josh. "It's nearly Christmas, but not quite."

Grandpa nodded knowingly and took another bite of his cookie.

"These are very nice," he remarked. "I like chocolate chip cookies."

"I've done most of my Christmas shopping," continued Lauren, trying to steer him back to the important subject.

"Is it Christmas again already?" Grandpa responded. "Comes round quickly, doesn't it? Have another cookie. They're nice. I like chocolate chip cookies."

"Yes, so do I," agreed Josh. "We'll get some in for Christmas."

"You're coming to us for Christmas," added Lauren.

"Yes," said Grandpa. "I don't remember having chocolate chip cookies when I was a lad. Have you come straight from school?"

"Yes," they chorused.

"I hated school as a lad," reflected Grandpa.

Lauren and Josh glanced at each other in despair. How could they keep Grandpa on the subject of Christmas?

"Did you use to write a letter to Santa?" prompted Lauren desperately.

Grandpa looked blank and then grimaced.

"Don't you mean Father Christmas?" he challenged her. "Always used to call him Father Christmas."

"Yes. Father Christmas," Lauren encouraged him.

She beamed at Josh. They were getting somewhere at last.

"No," said Grandpa. "The girl next door used to write letters to the fairies."

Lauren and Josh sighed.

"Gloria Jones, her name was," Grandpa enlightened them with a dreamy smile. "Pretty little thing. She was in the same class as me at school."

Lauren and Josh waited expectantly. They might as well just let him talk.

"Had a dolls' house," Grandpa continued. "Oh, I did envy her that dolls' house."

"Really?" exclaimed Lauren before she could stop herself.

"She never put her dolls in it," Grandpa explained hurriedly. "The rooms and furniture were far too small for dolls. So don't go thinking I was a big sissy or anything."

Josh looked shocked. Lauren grinned at him.

"No political correctness in those days," she hissed.

"Shouldn't call them dolls' houses really," lamented Grandpa. "They're just miniature houses with miniature furniture. I liked rearranging the rooms. Nothing sissy about *that,* is there?"

They shook their heads solemnly.

Grandpa chuckled to himself.

"Gloria got really fed up with me," he chortled. "I used to keep going round to her place just so that I could play with her dolls' house. I completely ignored her. I was only interested in the house. She couldn't get near it."

He was momentarily lost in sad reflection.

"She banned me from playing with it in the end."

Then he laughed again.

"She'd been saying for months that she was going to marry me," he finished his story. "But she got so sick of me monopolising her dolls' house that she called the wedding off!"

He paused and eyed his grandchildren mischievously.

"Just as well really," he informed them gleefully. "Or I wouldn't have married your grandmother and then your father wouldn't have been born. And nor would you for that matter. I always vowed I would buy my children a dolls' house, but I had boys and they didn't want one. Said it was sissy, just like my parents did."

Josh was squirming uncomfortably. The word *sissy* offended him, whereas Lauren found it amusing.

They never did get Grandpa back on to the subject of Christmas, but Lauren didn't mind. She had an idea and was very pleased with it.

"Things are much better nowadays than in Grandpa's day, aren't they?" declared Josh as they walked home. "People are free to be their true selves instead of having to worry about being called sissy and stuff, or being made fun of for being different."

"*Are* they free to be their true selves though?" countered Lauren. "Haven't you ever been teased? Haven't you ever been made to feel small or *wrong* just because of your position on something?"

Josh conceded reluctantly that he had.

"Political correctness only protects certain ideals and certain people," Lauren proclaimed grandly. "You're only free to be your true self if your true self fits the profile of what's acceptable. It's just as intolerant and narrow-minded as the old attitudes in many ways."

Josh opened and closed his mouth in a passionate desire to put Lauren straight, but when she was in full big sister mode he knew there was no competing with her, so he backed down.

"We still haven't solved Christmas," he grumbled. "We still don't know how to make it extra special for Grandpa."

"Yes, we do," sang Lauren. "He's handed it to us on a plate."

She paused to savour Josh's grudging curiosity before putting him out of his misery.

"We'll smarten up my old dolls' house and give it to Grandpa for Christmas!" she told him excitedly. "It's at the back of my cupboard, taking up loads of space. I've been meaning to get rid of it for ages. Let's do it up for Grandpa. I've still got the furniture somewhere, and we can buy him a bit more if we need to. We can pool the money we would have spent on an ordinary present for him, so we'll have enough funds."

Josh swallowed his pride and congratulated Lauren with genuine appreciation.

Grandpa was delighted with his dolls' house and set it up on the table straight away so that he could start playing with it without delay. He picked up a small chair and fumbled as he attempted to place it in the house.

Lauren experienced a crushing moment of heart-breaking doubt. What if Grandpa's hands weren't nimble enough to cope with miniature furniture anymore? She hadn't thought of that. It would ruin the present and cause Grandpa distress instead of making him happy.

"Here, let me help you," offered Josh, catching the look of anguish on his sister's face.

He walked towards the table but Grandpa shooed him away.

"I can manage," he growled. "Always were fiddly things. It's just a knack."

Grandpa kept calm and persevered and, after a few minutes, was arranging the furniture without any real difficulty at all.

"See?" he said triumphantly, glancing round at his anxious audience. "There's life in the old dog yet."

Grandpa played contentedly with his dolls' house throughout the whole of Christmas Day, taking just a few little breaks every now and then to eat or have a snooze.

"No wonder Gloria Jones got sick of him," whispered Lauren joyfully to Josh.

"Do you know something?" announced Grandpa when it was almost bedtime. "I believe this is the finest present I've ever had. In fact I think I could go as far as to say this is the best Christmas I've ever had. And I've had quite a lot of Christmases!"

20. Christmas Shopping

I planned all my shopping
With foresight and care
- No dread of a panic
No risk of despair
I'd saved up my money
And budgeted well
Then browsed round to see
What the shops had to sell
I made a full list
With a gift by each name
The presents were varied
Not one was the same

And so I set off
With my money and list
But quickly encountered
An unwelcome twist
The first shop was empty
Or so it appeared
Large gaps filled the shelves
Where the stocks had been cleared
The items I wanted
- Intended to buy -
Had all been snapped up
And I feared I might cry

The second shop likewise
Had nothing of use
"You've left it too late"
Came the feeble excuse
In shop after shop
I was quashed in my quest
Their goods had sold out
It was hard to digest
My plans had been thwarted
My hard work had failed
My list was redundant
My shopping derailed

Folk still needed presents
So what could be done?
My festive excursion
Was no longer fun
I'd have to review it
Buy *something* – but *what*?
My mind lurched and froze
I was losing the plot
… A book for each child
Plus a notepad and pen
Boxed "smellies" for ladies
And socks for the men

21. Christmas With No Money

Emma took one last, sad look at her beloved catalogue and tossed it into the recycling bin. It was a wonderful catalogue. She had browsed through it over and over again. It was the most exciting Christmas catalogue she had ever seen, but she would never be able to afford to buy anything from it, so why keep it just to torment herself?

She returned dejectedly to the house. What kind of Christmas would she be able to give her children? She struggled to feed and clothe them on a day-to-day basis. Christmas was way out of her league.

Riley wasn't quite five and Bella had only just turned three. They *had* to experience the thrill of Christmas. They *had* to have a visit from Santa.

Money had always been tight, but since Emma's partner had abandoned her for another woman, her finances had become scarily tricky to handle.

She fished the catalogue out of the bin again. Just flicking through it lifted her spirits. It filled her head with images of happy children opening intriguing parcels and squealing with pleasure as they played with their new toys.

Even the "stocking fillers" were outrageously expensive, many of them costing more than she would expect to spend on a main present even if she had plenty of money – which, of course, she didn't.

Emma sighed and dropped the catalogue back into the recycling bin. There was no point in torturing herself. She would somehow have to manage a very low budget Christmas. It would test her resourcefulness to its limits.

Her mother had always praised her for her imagination and resourcefulness. This was a good time to prove how imaginative and resourceful she could be. It would be a challenge. She enjoyed a challenge – or at least she *used* to enjoy a challenge before life became one big challenge.

Her family would be willing to help her out. She knew that. She wasn't as alone as many people in her situation. But her family had warned her against getting involved with the selfish rat who had deserted her, and she was too proud to go begging to them after he had behaved in exactly the way they had said he would.

She switched her mood from hopeless to optimistic, from self-pitying to determined. She would do it! She would give her children the most exciting Christmas ever, without spending any extra money.

Yes, and then she would write a "How To" book about it. It would be a bestseller for sure. She would make a fortune. She would become a household name. She would –

Actually, no, she didn't want to become a household name. She would prefer to remain anonymous … and she certainly didn't want The Rat to find out about her success.

She would publish under a pseudonym. That would solve the problem.

Now all she needed to do was work out how to give her children the most exciting Christmas ever, without spending any extra money.

"This is a boat," announced Bella, holding up a cardboard carton as Emma returned to the living-room.

"I thought it was a doll's bed," said Emma, smiling.

"It's a boat now," Riley told her grandly. "Can we sail it in the bath?"

"No, darling. It's cardboard. It'll get soggy and sink."

The children looked so downcast that Emma didn't know whether to laugh or cry.

"I know!" she told them brightly. "We'll make a *plastic* boat!"

She ran back out to the recycling bin and rummaged around until she found a plastic carton with no holes in it and no rough or sharp edges for the children to damage themselves on. Then she heaved her large roasting tin out of the cupboard – she couldn't remember the last time she used *that* – and spread some bin liners across the kitchen floor.

By this time the children were watching her quizzically. Emma grinned. She felt like a magician. She placed the roasting tin on top of the bin liners and then filled it with water, using a jug rather than risking sloshing water all over the place by putting it straight in the tin from the tap.

An idea was forming in her mind, and the more she chewed it over the more she liked it. Riley and Bella loved playing with boxes and cartons and tubes. They made all sorts of interesting toys and games out of them. Once they got going, and let their imaginations run wild, they were remarkably inventive – and, yes, resourceful, like their mother.

For Christmas Santa would bring them lots and lots of boxes and cartons and tubes. She would see what the shops could spare her. She would ask the neighbours – the friendly ones – to save her things. It would be the best present ever.

Meanwhile the boat had got into difficulties. The sea had become rough and the boat was filling with water.

"It's going to drown!" squealed Bella gleefully, scooping some more water into the boat to make sure it *did* drown.

"You said *cardboard* would sink, not *plastic*," teased Riley with an impish smile.

Emma was about to flick water into his face, but stopped herself just in time. That would be silly in the extreme. The last thing she wanted to do was encourage two small children to throw water around inside the house!

Emma felt happy. Blissfully happy. She had solved Christmas. She didn't even need to worry about an extravagant Christmas lunch. She could just give the children their favourite meal – chicken nuggets and baked beans – and then as a special treat they could have chocolate mousse for pudding. Yes, and they could make chocolate crispie cakes together on Christmas Eve to eat on

Christmas afternoon instead of Christmas cake. Riley and Bella didn't like rich fruit cake anyway, and Emma wasn't all that keen on it either.

The shops and neighbours were kind and accommodating way beyond Emma's dreams or expectations, supplying Emma with boxes, cartons and tubes of all shapes and sizes. They applauded her ingenuity and sensible approach and wanted to do everything possible to support her.

One lady, two doors away, offered to store all the goodies in her spare bedroom, well away from inquisitive young eyes, and bring them round on Christmas Eve after the children had gone to bed. She even provided a huge double bedspread to cover them with.

"And I've got an *enormous* box that some gardening equipment came in," she declared eagerly. "They can turn it into a house or a den or something. They'll have a whale of a time."

Of course, the box project meant that Santa's presents wouldn't fit into a pillow case or sack, but there were plenty of gifts from relatives and friends, so the children would still have lots of parcels to open.

Just after six o'clock on Christmas morning Riley and Bella burst exuberantly into the living-room, confident that Santa had paid them a visit. Emma was gripped by a sudden panic. What if her brilliant idea hadn't been such a brilliant idea after all? What if they felt cheated? What if –

"Wow!" exclaimed the children as one as they lifted the bedspread and peeped underneath it. "Wow!"

They were so ecstatic they were lost for words, but their eyes were shining as they turned to look at her, and their faces more animated than she had ever seen them.

Yes, it *was* a brilliant idea, Emma complimented herself. There was absolutely no doubt about it.

The children played companionably with their boxes, cartons and tubes right up to bedtime. Emma had never known them to be so enthusiastic or so lost in their own magical world.

"I *love* Christmas," sighed Riley, his face radiant.

"Can we have more Christmas tomorrow?" asked Bella beseechingly. "Please!"

22. What Is Christmas?

"What is Christmas?" asked the stranger
"I'm not sure I understand
There's a sense of great excitement
Spreading all across the land"
"We just do it," came the answer
- And it made the stranger sigh
"It's a habit. It's tradition
But I couldn't tell you why"

"What is Christmas?" asked the stranger
Of another standing near
"There's a sense of celebration
Glee and merriment. Good cheer"
"It's a time for food and parties"
Came the answer. "Drinking too
We have lights and decorations
It's just something that we do"

"What is Christmas?" asked the stranger
Of a child with thoughtful stare
"There's a sense of expectation
I can feel it in the air"
"It's a special person's birthday
From a long, long time ago
And the children wait for Santa
I'm surprised you didn't know"

"Tell me more," implored the stranger
"I'm still puzzled. Please explain"
"Baby Jesus," came the answer
"He's a king who didn't reign
He's the Prince of Peace, they reckon
He's God's Son. From Up Above
Jesus came to make us better
And to teach us how to love

God gave Jesus as a present
It's His party. Christmas Day
That's why *Santa* brings us presents
He calls by but doesn't stay
And we're meant to help each other
And be kind to friend and foe
Jesus wants us to be happy
I'm surprised you didn't know"

23. In The Bleak Mid-December

For a couple of years, I played a cornet in my Junior School brass band. We didn't have a school uniform, but we did have a band uniform. This consisted of a white shirt, green tie and dark grey/black skirt (girls) or trousers (boys). There was no jumper, cardigan or jacket because we always performed indoors.

One December, when I was about nine, we were booked to play carols to shoppers in the town centre, thereby breaking from tradition and venturing outdoors. We were thrilled to be doing something so special for Christmas, and all the more excited because we would be missing lessons. The day dawned bleak and drizzly. There was a strong icy wind and it was bitterly cold. We weren't allowed to wear coats as we walked from school to the square because there would be nowhere to put them, and coats were not part of our strict "performing" uniform. We were frozen.

We began to play *Christians Awake*, glancing round eagerly for a glimpse of our appreciative audience. The square was deserted. Eventually two elderly ladies emerged from a shop. They peered at us curiously for a moment and then moved on. As far as I was aware, nobody else took any interest in us the whole time we were there.

Our fingers were so stiff and sore we could hardly press the valves on our instruments. The violent wind kept whipping our music off the stands, prompting children to flit backwards and forwards on a frantic rescue mission. The teacher darted among us handing out clothes pegs so that we could pin the music down. He ran out of clothes pegs long before all the music was secure.

Then a few half-hearted snowflakes descended on us. The teacher's face lit up. "Play *See Amid the Winter's Snow*!" he cried jubilantly. This was not on our prepared schedule. "Play *See Amid the Winter's Snow*!" It made me smile. It redeemed the morning. Our exciting contribution to the community's Christmas celebrations had been a miserable disaster, but suddenly I felt happy again. We played *See Amid the Winter's Snow* with gusto and, to this day, I can't sing that carol without being reminded of our music teacher's innocent enthusiasm as he responded gleefully to a mini snow shower on that bitterly cold, blustery December morning in the desolate town centre.

24. Something Missing

The fairy lights were twinkling
I'd beautified the tree
But something still was missing
Whatever could it be?

My gifts were wrapped and labelled
My cards all written too
But something still was missing
Whatever could I do?

My special food was ready
Of that I had no doubt
But something still was missing
I couldn't work it out

Arrangements were completed
The jobs had all been done
Yet something still was missing
Though Christmas had begun

I sang myself a carol
And felt my joy increase
I thought of Baby Jesus
And found my inner peace

25. Keeping Things In Perspective

I'd listed what still needed doing
I wanted so much to be ready
Without getting flustered or fretful
My motto: Calm, Happy and Steady

I wanted it all to be perfect
Uplifting, with everyone cheerful
But things kept on turning against me
My motto became Cross and Tearful

My trimmings, initially pleasing
Seemed suddenly clumsy, half-hearted
The cards looked untidily scattered
My inner peace swiftly departed

The tree was unbalanced and messy
I couldn't dissuade it from leaning
And after my wild, vain adjustments
The freshly vacked floor needed cleaning

My light-up church wouldn't illumine
My CD of carols kept skipping
The thermostat failed on the oven
My gift wrap just wouldn't stop ripping

I'd treated myself to a bargain
- Some fudge (peanut butter and honey)
But when I succumbed to temptation
I realised I'd wasted my money

A neighbour requested assistance
Then someone stopped by for a natter
I never got round to my baking
- But surely it's *people* that matter

I need to keep things in perspective
I need to remember the reason
- The joy and the hope and the promise -
Behind my delight in the season

So what if the tree looks lopsided
And most of the tinsel is moulting
The cards are uneven – and frankly
That cheap fudge is truly revolting?

So what if the oven needs fixing
And most of my wrapping is bitty?
I have other Christmas recordings
My non-glowing church is still pretty

That first Christmas didn't go smoothly
Poor Mary! She must have been frantic
A long way from home. Dirty. Weary
It certainly wasn't romantic!

For Jesus was born in a stable
And lay on the hay in a manger
A helpless, defenceless new baby
Yet now we revere that small stranger

And if we could act on His message
- Love, peace and goodwill, gracious giving
The future would surely look brighter
And life would feel much more worth living

26. Drop-In Christmas

It was a blustery day – yet another one - and certainly not the best weather for putting up posters outside. However it had to be done. She had put it off for too long already in the hope that the strong winds would abate, but they showed no sign of doing so.

A sudden violent gust snatched the laminated poster from her hand and flung it across the road. A teenage girl jumped up gracefully and caught it as it attempted to pass her.

She brought it back to Maria, waving it triumphantly in the air.

"Thank you!" said Maria with heartfelt gratitude. "You're a star. That was very impressive, and very kind."

"Not really," responded the girl dismissively. She pointed at the poster. "So are you doing this Drop-In Centre Christmas Lunch actually on Christmas Day then?"

"Yes," replied Maria eagerly, glad that someone was showing an interest. "For people who are on their own. Homeless even. People who wouldn't have much fun otherwise."

The girl weighed it up and then nodded approvingly.

"Now that *is* kind," she declared. "We don't do Christmas at our house."

Maria was shocked.

"Don't you?" she asked, surprised. "Is it against your religion?"

The girl looked puzzled.

"Religion?" she queried. "Against my *religion*? No. Nothing to do with that. Don't think I've got a religion. No, it's not that."

Maria raised her eyebrows questioningly. She didn't want to pry, but she was curious.

"Not worth the hassle," the girl enlightened her cheerfully. "Too expensive. Mum getting stressed out about everything. Too much eating and drinking. People getting drunk and doing stupid things and violent things. Everyone arguing. There's just no point in it. We haven't bothered with it since I was eight or nine."

"What a shame," remarked Maria sympathetically.

"Not really," chirped the girl. "I used to hate it anyway. Like I said, too much hassle."

"It doesn't have to be like that," sighed Maria, feeling out of her depth.

"It does in *our* family," laughed the girl. "Christmas brings out the worst in people. Don't you reckon?"

Maria felt silly. What a foolish comment to have made to a young girl who clearly had a difficult home life.

"It shouldn't bring out the worst in people," she mumbled, her enthusiasm quashed. "But I know what you mean."

"The daft thing is my name means Christmas," the girl threw out. "Natalie. A bit of a joke really, seeing as we don't do Christmas."

She stood silently for a moment, reading the poster.

"Is it just food you're doing, or are you giving them a party as well?" she enquired. "You ought to have games and stuff. They'll enjoy that. Particularly if they don't usually have much fun."

"Yes, they'll be playing games as well," Maria assured her. "Those who want to, that is. And singing Christmas songs as well."

Natalie was looking thoughtful.

"Pass the Parcel!" she exclaimed suddenly. "You've got to have *that*! Pass the Parcel was my favourite party game when I was little. Never won the prize, mind you."

Maria was dubious.

"They'll all be adults -," she began to explain.

"Doesn't matter," Natalie interrupted. "They'll love it. Trust me. They'll *love* it. I'll do it for you if you like."

Maria opened her mouth to protest, but Natalie didn't give her chance.

"You know that cheap shop near the Post Office?" she continued. "Well, they've got packets of wrapping paper with loads of sheets in and it hardly costs anything. I was looking at them the other day and thinking that's what I would buy if I bothered with Christmas."

She paused briefly.

"I'll get the present as well if you like," she concluded. "I've got a bit of money left over from my birthday. We *do* birthdays in our family. Just not Christmas."

"That's very kind of you," spluttered Maria, not sure how to take this extraordinary teenager.

"Not really," responded Natalie dismissively. "We won't have forfeits. Don't want to embarrass anyone. I used to hate forfeits in Pass the Parcel, even though I was a big show-off."

Neither spoke for a moment. Maria was rehearsing a question in her mind. She hardly dared ask, but -

"Will you come to the Christmas lunch, Natalie?" she hazarded. "Even though you don't do Christmas? Would your mum mind?"

"Course she wouldn't," answered Natalie. "Why would she? Course I'll come. How can I supervise Pass the Parcel if I'm not there?"

She looked troubled.

"Will you be able to sort out the music?"

Maria nodded. She was wondering what kind of prize a teenage girl would come up. It needed to be something that would be suitable for *anybody* who might win it. Would Natalie think of that? Maria didn't want to undermine Natalie's confidence by checking up on her, so she kept quiet.

On Christmas morning Natalie turned up well in advance of the agreed time. She sported a festive apron, thanks to the cheap shop near the Post Office, and had tinsel in her hair – also thanks to the cheap shop near the Post Office. For someone who didn't do Christmas she was full of Christmas cheer.

"We're going to give them the best Christmas ever," she announced with passion. "Poor things. That's the least we can do for them."

What a generous-hearted young girl! thought Maria.

The parcel was enormous.

"It's got twenty layers," Natalie informed her proudly. "It was a bit of a squeeze by the end, mind you. Good job they're big sheets of paper."

"What's *in* there?" gasped Maria, unable to contain herself any longer.

Natalie grinned mysteriously. Was she planning to keep it a secret? Maria hoped not. She couldn't bear the suspense any longer.

"*Please*! Put me out of my misery!" she begged.

Natalie chortled.

"Knew you'd ask if I kept you dangling," she teased. "It's a scarf. A thick, cosy, long one in lots of bright colours. Cheer them up a bit. And if they're on their own their house is probably cold, isn't it?"

Maria smiled at the youngster's logic.

"And if they're homeless they'll *definitely* need something warm," Natalie concluded. "I knitted it myself. I quite like knitting. Got the wool from that cheap shop near the Post Office. Bags with loads of different colours in. Really cheap."

Maria made a mental note to go and investigate the cheap shop near the Post Office as soon as the holiday was over.

"A scarf sounds perfect," she congratulated her new friend. "Well done."

Natalie proved a great hit with the guests, most of whom were elderly, and likewise with the other helpers. She threw herself into the celebrations heart and soul, waiting on tables, chatting to people – and, of course, her *pièce de résistance*, treating them to a hilarious game of Pass the Parcel. There were whoops and giggles and shrieks of delight.

Maria surveyed the scene with deep satisfaction. Everyone looked happy and excited and animated. It might not be the best Christmas *ever*, but for many of these people it was undoubtedly the best Christmas they had experienced in a very long time.

Maria wished she had thought to bring a gift for Natalie, although she suspected this exceptional girl wouldn't have wanted to be rewarded that way. In fact she might even have been offended. No. It was probably better to just say *thank you*

"Are we doing it again next year?" asked Natalie eagerly as they said *good-bye* to the last of the guests.

"I sincerely hope so," replied Maria.

27. Candle-Lit Carols

Cosy in a holy setting
Sheltered from the evening chill
Dancing flames enhanced by darkness
Atmosphere that gives a thrill

Carol after much loved carol
Sung with gusto, voiced with joy
Stirring tunes evoking feelings
Welcoming a baby boy

Once in royal David's city
Hark! The herald-angels sing
Angels, from the realms of glory
Worshipping the new-born king

Cheering, soothing, reassuring
Well-known words, yet ever new
Golden oldies tried and trusted
Warming hearts the service through

Scripture readings interspersing
Words well-known, yet ever new
Telling us the Christmas story
Baby Jesus, born a Jew

Tunes uplifting, words inspiring
Feeding spirit, mind and soul
Healing for our fractured beings
Christmas *can* still make us whole

28. A Present For Santa

"Does Santa get any presents?" asked Harvey suddenly.

Ruby hesitated before answering. She was six years older than Harvey and took the responsibility very seriously. It was vitally important to respond appropriately.

"Does Jesus put up a stocking for Santa?" Harvey added before Ruby had spoken.

"How should I know?" exclaimed Ruby.

"Just thought you might," mumbled Harvey sulkily.

"Well, I don't," retorted Ruby.

Then she was annoyed with herself for handling the conversation so badly. She had always tried to deal with Harvey in a grown-up style and speak to him in a way that would protect his innocence and self-esteem. However, his increasingly challenging questions were making it very difficult for her.

"Why don't you give him a present anyway?" she suggested, feeling safer with the Santa issue than with the Jesus one. "People leave Santa refreshments. Why don't you put a little present for him as well?"

Harvey considered the idea for a moment.

"It's Jesus's birthday at Christmas, isn't it?" he threw out. "So he needs two presents, doesn't he? A Christmas present and a birthday present."

Ruby sighed.

"I suppose so," she agreed warily. "Why don't you *make* a present for Santa? Then it'll be something no one has ever given him before. That will be really special. He'll love that."

The pensive expression on Harvey's face was one that always caused Ruby to dread what he would come out with next. She braced herself as he opened his mouth.

"You mean like a new outfit or a new sleigh?"

Ruby composed herself.

"No," she replied calmly. "I was thinking more …"

She scanned the room desperately for inspiration and her eyes settled on a pile of pompoms.

"A pompom!" she finished triumphantly.

Harvey wasn't impressed.

"A pompom *reindeer*," Ruby elaborated. "That would be *really* special."

Harvey frowned, looking interested.

"Like Rudolph?" he probed. "With a red nose?"

"Exactly," confirmed Ruby, trying to hide her relief.

"Will you help me with the antlers?"

"Yes, of course I will."

Ruby felt pleased with herself. Wow. She'd handled that well. It would be easy and quick to create a pompom reindeer with a red nose.

They set to work straight away. Harvey made the pompom on his own. Pompom craft being his new hobby, he didn't require any assistance. However when it came to the face and the antlers he invited Ruby to take charge.

Together they transformed the plain brown pompom into a cheerful red-nosed reindeer. Its face was a bit wonky, but Harvey was happy with it and Ruby proclaimed that it gave the reindeer character.

They decided not to wrap the reindeer up. It would be more welcoming to Santa if he could see its friendly face watching out for him.

Next Harvey needed to write a letter so that Santa would know the reindeer was for him. He composed the letter himself, but allowed Ruby to help him with the spelling so that he didn't make any mistakes.

Dear Santa,

Here is a present for you. I made it myself specially and Ruby helped me. I hope you like it. Please remember to give Jesus two presents. It's his birthday at Christmas, so he needs a birthday present and a Christmas present. Merry Christmas.

Love Harvey.

P.S. You can have a biscuit if you want one.

Just before Harvey's bedtime they put the reindeer and letter next to a glass of milk and a plate of biscuits on the dining-room table.

"Do you think he'll find it?" asked Harvey anxiously. "My stocking's in the other room."

Ruby nodded confidently and then, touched by Harvey's worried little face, came up with the perfect solution.

"I'll pin a note to your stocking telling him to check in the dining-room," she promised.

Harvey was satisfied, although he wouldn't go to bed until he'd seen the note and attached it to the stocking himself.

On Christmas morning Harvey was so concerned about his gift for Santa that he didn't give a thought to his own stocking. Instead he headed straight for the dining-room to see whether Santa had found his pompom reindeer.

"It's gone!" Harvey shrieked gleefully within seconds of entering the room. "It's gone! He came and he found it!"

Ruby rushed to join him. Harvey was clutching a piece of paper, his eyes shining.

"It's a letter from Santa," he whispered, almost over-awed by the thrill of the moment. "In his own actual handwriting. I'll keep it for ever. Look."

Ruby reached out for the letter, but Harvey didn't release his hold on it, so she just peered over his shoulder instead.

Dear Harvey,

Thank you for my special present. I don't get many presents and my pompom reindeer is the nicest thing I have ever been given. You were very clever to make it yourself.

I gave Jesus two presents like you asked me to. My presents to Jesus were two promises. One promise was to love everybody and the other promise was to be kind to everybody. That might sound a bit strange, but those are the kinds of presents Jesus likes.

Warmest regards,

Santa

Harvey gazed up at his big sister earnestly.

"Nobody else in the *whole world* has got a letter like that from Santa, have they?" he sighed ecstatically.

"Definitely not," agreed Ruby.

29. Special Days

I love Christmas Eve
For its promise and hope
Its last-minute fun preparation
The childlike excitement
As nightfall draws near
The wonderful anticipation

I love Christmas Day
For its joy and goodwill
Its heart-warming message for living
Church, fellowship, loved ones
Fine food, presents, treats
A time for receiving and giving

When Boxing Day comes
I feel tranquil, relaxed
And love it for being more leisured
No need for perfection
Calm, gentle, less stress
A day to be valued and treasured

30. No Room At The Inn

There's no room at the inn
Nowhere cosy to stay
Just a stable for shelter
And manger of hay
But there's room in our hearts
If we want it that way
And He'll settle straight in
If we ask Him to stay

There's no room at the inn
Anguished pleas won't be heard
Just the lowing of livestock
The song of a bird
But there's room in our minds
If we just say the word
He'll support us and listen
Our cries *will* be heard

There's no room at the inn
Town's too busy. Who cares?
People paying their taxes
Some touting their wares
But there's room in our lives
In our daily affairs
If we just make Him welcome
We'll see that He cares

31. The Infallible List

"Right. Surely nothing can go wrong now," Di told herself proudly, "As long as they all turn up at the right time and behave themselves."

And if they didn't, that would hardly be Di's fault, would it? She couldn't be blamed if other people spoiled things for her.

Her daughter and grandson, who would be staying for a couple of nights, had already arrived. The rest of the guests were due mid-morning on Christmas Day. Julie, Di's daughter, was out visiting friends, but had been given strict instructions to return by ten-thirty, to give Di and her husband time to get to church without any rush or panic.

Di had planned Christmas down to the last detail. The turkey was organised. The presents were wrapped – had been for three weeks. The mince pies and sausage rolls and shortbread and chocolate log were ready. Christmas cake … Christmas pudding … vegetables under control … well, everything was as it should be at this stage.

She had checked her list several times. It was a list she had compiled many, many years before and it had never failed her. She could relax for a few minutes.

No she couldn't relax. Christmas wasn't a time for relaxing. There was too much to do. There was too great a risk of something going wrong if she let her guard down.

She looked at her watch anxiously. Almost quarter past ten.

No she couldn't relax. Not until Julie had put in an appearance. If Di couldn't get to Midnight Communion it would mess up her plans completely.

Little Noah was safely tucked up in bed. He had labelled his pillow case – confident, bless him, that Santa would have no difficulty reading his writing and recognising his name - and had been sound asleep for three hours, unless he was an extremely good actor. Di had peeped in on him at regular intervals and he hadn't stirred. Despite his excitement and his determination to listen for the sleigh bells, Noah had dropped off to sleep almost the second his head hit the pillow.

Di herself just had to get church over with and then she could concentrate fully on Christmas. A practising Christian, she considered it important to attend church over Christmas, despite how busy she was, but she always opted for the Christmas Eve Midnight Communion service so that she could keep Christmas Day clear for the important practicalities and festivities of the celebration.

A car drew up. It was Julie. What a relief! Di sat back and breathed in the calm air. She would make the most of a few peaceful moments. There would be precious few of them the following day. It would be noisy and chaotic – and very tiring – but hopefully happy and successful.

It was a very short night, but that was to be expected. It was almost one o'clock when they got back from church. Then they were up soon after six o'clock for Noah to see what Santa had brought.

Di wouldn't have slept much anyway, even if she'd had longer in bed. Christmas was far too tense a time for repose. Everything had to be right. Everything had to be perfect. She had checked her list so carefully. Surely nothing could go wrong.

All the guests turned up within twenty minutes of their scheduled arrival times. The meal was splendid as always. If anything, she had excelled herself. Di knew she shouldn't blow her own trumpet, but she was an outstanding cook. There was no getting away from it. And she was renowned for her prowess as a hostess. Visitors invariably congratulated her on what a wonderful time they had had.

The adults' gift opening ceremony, although not as thrilling as Noah's foray into Santa's sack, was gratifyingly enjoyable. This was followed by games, which were accompanied by non-stop laughter and jollity. The day flew by.

At last Di allowed herself to relax. She was finally "off duty". Things were winding down.

They had eaten, drunk and made merry and the guests would soon be returning to their own homes, except for Julie and Noah.

Di sat back and reflected on her efforts and meticulous preparations and felt pleased with herself.

Well, that was that for another year. Everything had gone well and according to plan. It had been a success. Di surveyed her surroundings and felt slightly uncomfortable.

Everywhere she turned there were people lolling around, looking bloated and glazed over. There were so many gifts. So many discarded wrappings. There was so much left-over food. So much washing-up. The whole scene yelled over-indulgence. Even sunny little Noah had become sullen and fractious, suffering from the effects of too many presents, too many treats and too much excitement.

Di slept well that night, and woke the next morning feeling refreshed and rested. She lay with her eyes closed, wondering whether to allow herself the luxury of an extra half hour in bed.

"Grandma," whispered a young voice at her side. "Can we get up now?"

Di opened her eyes and smiled. There was Noah, just about visible in the glow of the plug-in nightlight on the landing. How long had he been standing there unnoticed?

"Yes, of course we can, darling," Di replied, almost relieved that the decision had been made for her.

They went downstairs and set the table ready for breakfast. Di was about to put the kettle on when a sudden cry of anguish stopped her in her tracks.

"Grandma!" shrieked Noah from the living-room.

Di abandoned the kettle and rushed to see what was wrong.

"Grandma!" squealed Noah. "You forgot Jesus! You forgot Jesus. Look!"

He pointed to the empty manger in the centre of Di's carefully arranged nativity scene.

"Where is He?"

"Must have left Him in the box," muttered Di, deeply embarrassed.

She made a mental note to add JESUS to her infallible Christmas check-list.

32. All That Glitters

I bought a roll of Christmas wrap
It sparkled and it glistened
Its silver swirls enchanted me
I eulogised. It listened
And on the back were scissor lines
To help me with the cutting
Good! That would stop me floundering
And messing up and tutting

This paper was good quality
Its length and width extensive
It cost me hardly anything
Yet should have been expensive
Well – maybe it was last year's stock
And needed selling cheaply
It puzzled me – though not enough
To make me ponder deeply

I settled down on Christmas Eve
- Quite late - to do my wrapping
The paper folded easily
With edges overlapping
My parcels looked spectacular
Their beauty was beguiling
No need for bright embellishments
I gazed upon them smiling

Then one by one they bounced undone
My presents were escaping!
My silver swirls had *Attitude*
I reinforced my taping
Then as before the parcels popped
And each one sat there yawning
My tantrums were in vain, so too my
My pleading and my fawning

The paper hated sticky tape
And kept on misbehaving
Refusing to be anchored - quite
Immune to anguished raving
No ribbon, bows or glue had I
No other means of wrapping
It seemed the only answer was
Some heavy-duty strapping

A ball of string was all I found
No wool – I'm not a knitter
I'd fix those parcels, come what may
I'd triumph! I'm no quitter
The string worked well, though true to say
It wasn't very pretty
My silver swirls were not enhanced
- *Their* fault - but what a pity!

33. Reindeer Rant

Now don't get me wrong. I've got nothing against Rudolph – he's a great guy - and his glowing red nose really does come in handy on a foggy night, but why does *he* get all the attention and adulation? We're a *team*. We all play our part. It isn't just down to him, you know. We're *all* important.

And, to be honest, Rudolph's got no sense of direction at all. He'd get us lost in no time if *he* took charge. *I'm* the one who navigates. *I'm* the one who remembers the route and the order we're supposed to be doing things in. *I'm* the one who decides the best place to land on the roofs. Believe me, Santa would be in a right mess if he relied on Rudolph's judgement all the time.

Like I said, Rudolph's a great guy. Don't get me wrong. And his sense of humour has helped us through many a difficult Christmas Eve. I mean, I remember one year when everything was going wrong … violent winds trying to push us off course … parcels bouncing out of the sleigh – and it wasn't *Rudolph* who rescued them either … threatening letters from naughty children who still wanted presents even though they hadn't even *tried* to be good … and then Santa got bitten on the bottom by a feisty chihuahua … I tell you, it was all happening. And just when we were feeling really fed up and like we couldn't take any more, Rudolph told us this hilarious joke about a rude child who got kidnapped by a gang of chihuahuas. And we all laughed so much we nearly crashed into a space observatory.

But, like I said, it isn't *all* about Rudolph. We're a team. He couldn't do it on his own, you know. It's tiring work. We *all* get worn out. And it's hungry work too. Some people sprinkle reindeer food on the ground or roof for all of us to share, which is brilliant, but don't think the rest of us haven't noticed how many children only leave out a carrot for *Rudolph*. Just for Rudolph, mind you. Nobody else. I mean – what's that about? Don't they care about *me*? Don't they care about the other reindeer? *We* get hungry too. *We* work hard too. Rudolph couldn't deliver all those presents on his own, you know. So why only a carrot for *Rudolph*? Why should *he* get all the credit?

Like I said, Rudolph's a great guy. But come on, folks. Give the rest of us a break.

34. Where Is Christmas?

Where is the joy? Where is the peace?
Where is the love and goodwill?
Why are we sad? Why are we lost?
Why are we arguing still?
Love fosters peace. Peace fosters joy
Goodwill illumines the way
Love, peace, goodwill. Joy - life's a *gift*
- Hope *can* thrive, even today

35. The Best Present Ever

"I've asked Santa for a smartphone," announced Megan grandly.

"Well, he won't bring you one," muttered Mum.

"Yes he will," Megan contradicted her. "I've been good and I haven't even asked him for anything else."

"He won't bring you a smartphone," Mum insisted. "He'll bring you something different instead. It's not for you to know what."

"But *why*?" cried Megan. "*Why* won't he bring me a smartphone? I haven't even asked him for anything else. I haven't been greedy."

"Because he knows you don't need one," replied Mum. "You're too young. He'll bring you something more suitable."

"I *do* need one!" wailed Megan. "And I'm not too young. I'm nearly nine. It's not fair. All my friends have got a smartphone."

"I doubt that very much," said Mum stiffly. "Anyway Santa knows you couldn't afford the *on-going costs* of a smartphone. So he won't bring you one."

Megan flounced out of the room and ran to her bedroom to sulk. She flung herself on to her bed and began to sob. It wasn't fair. Everyone else had a smartphone.

She'd been extra good so that Santa would be pleased with her. She hadn't asked him for anything else. It wasn't fair.

She sat up to blow her nose and her eyes were drawn to an object on her bedside cupboard. It was a packet of cat treats, bought for her beloved pet Toby as a Christmas present. But Toby had disappeared. She hadn't seen him for two days.

New tears trickled down her cheeks, tears of grief replacing the tears of frustration.

"Where *are* you, Toby?" she called softly. "Come home. *Please*. I don't want Christmas without you."

He *would* come home. She had to believe that. She couldn't allow herself to fear that something bad had happened to him. She knew cats went missing sometimes. And mostly they came back. Didn't they?

It was Christmas Eve. Toby didn't have long to get himself home in time for Christmas. Where *was* he?

"He *will* come," she told herself firmly. "He *will* come. And Santa *will* bring me a smartphone."

She wrapped up Toby's present to prove to herself that she really, truly expected him home.

Bedtime came and there was still no sign of Toby.

Christmas morning arrived and there was still no sign of Toby. Megan looked sadly at his present, which she had placed lovingly under the tree, and her eyes filled with tears.

"Santa's been," sang Mum. "I wonder what he's brought you."

A smartphone! thought Megan gleefully. Santa *had* to have brought her a smartphone. It was the only thing that could take her mind off Toby.

She grabbed a parcel and poked it and shook it. It contained something soft, so it definitely wasn't a smartphone. That was okay. Her presents couldn't *all* be smartphones. That would be silly.

Megan fought her way into the parcel and lifted out a pair of brightly coloured pyjamas. She dropped them down impatiently and reached for the next parcel.

Pyjamas! What a boring thing to give as a present! She wore pyjamas every night of her life! What was so special about a pair of *pyjamas* for a Christmas present?

The next parcel was box shaped. Could *this* be the smartphone? She thought not. It was probably a bit big for a smartphone. No, it was Lego. Megan was disgusted. She'd grown out of Lego *ages* ago. Santa should have known that.

Another box. This was definitely too big for a smartphone. Megan gaped in disbelief as she opened it. A basket weaving kit! What was the point of a *basket weaving kit*? When had she ever wanted to weave baskets?

"What lovely presents, Megan," gushed Grandma. "What a lucky girl. Santa's been very kind to you."

Megan ignored her. They *weren't* lovely presents. She *wasn't* lucky. And Santa *hadn't* been kind to her. Not yet anyway. Where was her smartphone?

She rooted around and found a smaller box. Ah! This was more like it. *This* must be the smartphone.

Megan hesitated for moment, savouring the thrill of being on the verge of finding out what if felt like to have a smartphone all of her own at last. Then she tore wildly at the wrapping paper, her heart thumping. Impatiently, she extricated the box and examined it excitedly, turning it over and over as she searched for the magical word *Smartphone*.

Her heart sank as cruel realisation dawned. It wasn't a smartphone. It was an action camera. She tossed it to one side angrily. What did she need an *action camera* for? You could take action shots on a smartphone. Easily. You could take really good videos on a smartphone.

She didn't need an action camera. She just needed a smartphone. Then it hit her hard. Santa had brought her an action camera *instead* of a smartphone. She wasn't going to get a smartphone. Mum was right.

Megan hated Santa. She had only asked him for *one* thing and he hadn't even bothered to bring her that. She *hated* him. She *hated* him.

The doorbell rang. Mum jumped up to answer it. Megan followed sulkily, hoping it wasn't anyone she would have to be friendly to. She was in no mood to be friendly.

It was the lady from next-door-but-one, and she had a furry, tabby mound in her arms.

"Are you missing somebody?" she asked cheerily.

"Toby!" squealed Megan.

Toby lunged forward into Megan's waiting arms, purring rapturously.

"Sorry," said the lady. "You must have been frantic about him. He got himself shut in our shed. We went in a couple of days ago to clean down the garden chairs ready to use as extra seating when the visitors come. It was a bitterly cold, wet morning and Toby must have sneaked in for shelter and we shut him in without realising. We didn't open the shed again until just now when we went to fetch the chairs."

She smiled and stroked Toby under his chin.

"He doesn't seem any the worse for his adventure," she concluded.

Megan nestled her face into Toby's fur.

"This is the best Christmas present *ever*!" she declared.

No wonder Santa hadn't brought her a smartphone. He knew she would need to focus all her attention on Toby. Toby would have hated it if Megan had been messing around with a new smartphone all day.

Megan settled herself in a chair, fondling Toby, who was snuggled up in her lap. She couldn't remember ever feeling happier.

She looked across at her pile of parcels, some of them still unopened. The pyjamas were very cheerful and they looked cosy too. They were covered in big bright spots in all her favourite colours. She would enjoy wearing them. Her old pyjamas were getting very shabby and worn out.

The Lego set was a castle to build. It looked quite difficult, but it would be amazing when it was finished. She could make up a story about a beautiful princess – in spotted pyjamas – being locked up in a huge castle and needing someone brave to rescue her. She could play it out with her friends. She would be the princess ... or would she prefer to be the rescuer? No, she would be the princess. After all, they were *her* posh new pyjamas.

Her eyes lighted on the basket weaving kit. She had never tried making baskets before and, the more she thought about it, the more she likes the idea. It would be fun. And if she got really good at it she could make baskets as gifts for other people. Next Christmas *everyone* could have a basket and she wouldn't need to worry about what to give people.

Toby was gazing adoringly into her face, purring so loudly the joyful sound filled the room, and purring so hard his body was moving rhythmically as he did so.

Megan wished she had a video of Toby purring and – but she *could* have a video! Santa had brought her an action camera. She could take loads and loads of videos of Toby. She could video him washing and eating and drinking his water. She loved the delicate way he lapped at his water. And she could get him lapping his water on video to keep for ever.

And she could put an open paper bag on the carpet, in the middle of the room, and wait with her camera for him to pounce on it or try and dive inside it. She could film him playing with his ping pong ball and his toy mouse on a string. She could get Mum to video her having a cuddle with Toby. There were so many exciting things she could do with her new action camera.

Megan *loved* her presents. And she hadn't even opened them all yet. Santa had been very kind to her.

But her favourite present of all was having Toby back. That was the best present *ever*.

36. Christmas Morning

In the stillness of the darkness
There's excitement in the air
Lit-up houses tell a story
- Are the children busy there?

Are they opening their parcels?
Eager, hasty, full of glee?
As they dream of what's inside them
- Are they happy when they see?

Soon it's time for Christmas worship
Passing people in the street
Smiling faces, cheery greetings
Feeling love for all I meet

Then in church that sense of wonder
As we listen, sing and pray
What a thrill it always gives me
To be there on Christmas Day

Sense of fellowship uplifting
Hearts aglow with warmth and joy
As we celebrate the coming
Of that precious Baby Boy

37. Peace On Earth

Why can't we sort ourselves out? Is it really so hard to be nice to each other?

When I think of how easily I feel irritated, frustrated, impatient, undermined or upset, and how strong the compulsion is to explain my position, to justify myself and to help people understand that I'm in the right, it fills me with a terrible sense of despair and hopelessness. How will the promised "Peace on Earth" ever come if we can't, as individuals, curb our innate defensiveness?

I think my New Year's resolution should be to make a determined effort to rise above my own petty grievances. Will I go through with it? And, if so, how long will I keep it up?

38. Good-Bye 2020

It's been a strange year
With its problems and cares
Its heartache, confusion and grief
Its harsh disappointments
Frustrations and scares
We long for some sense of relief

We've mostly stayed cheerful
The best way we could
And handled *New Normals* galore
But life is for living
And needs to feel good
We long to act freely once more

We're keeping our distance
Protecting the weak
And striving to ward off the bugs
But life gets depressing
And prospects look bleak
We long for those kisses and hugs

A new year is looming
And stretches ahead
A time to look forward with hope?
Or are we discouraged?
And fearful instead?
And not at all certain we'll cope?

Let's make a shared promise
To come through this phase
By helping each other along
We'll weather dark moments
And difficult days
When pulling together we're strong

"Number five's done it on me now as well!" Danny wailed, stomping back into the house. "*She* used to keep *hers* up until twelfth night."

It was the afternoon of January 4th, officially the eleventh day of Christmas.

"Why couldn't she have left them up one more day?" he cried, fighting back tears. "Why did she have to spoil it? There's hardly anyone left. Why does everybody have to spoil it? Why can't they wait until twelfth night?"

"They're probably not thinking about the date," replied Saffie gently. "Don't take it too much to heart, Dan -"

"Danny," he corrected her. "Don't shorten it, like everyone shortens Christmas."

"Sorry," she said with a sheepish grin. "That's the weird thing, though, isn't it? They're not really *shortening* Christmas because they start so early on it. They lengthen it if anything."

Danny wiped away a tear.

"They've just changed the timing of it and the end date, that's all," Saffie continued. "For some people the whole of December is Christmas, and they get into it right at the beginning of the month and see New Year's Eve as the end. Others see New Year's Day as the last day – the end of the holiday - regardless of when they put their decorations up. Others vary it depending on when they go back to work, or what social plans they've got. I don't think many people worry about the twelfth night tradition anymore."

"Well they should," Danny sobbed.

Saffie sighed compassionately. She knew Danny well and understood his anguish.

Through the whole of his adult life he had struggled with mental health issues, mostly in the form of a combination of depression and anxiety, which fed on each other in a vicious circle. Somehow Christmas seemed to lift him out of that. Christmas gave him respite. It imbued him with a temporary sense of healing, exhilaration and freedom. Maybe that was why he clung to it so desperately.

"Anyway, there are still a few left," Saffie encouraged him. "Let's have a walk round when it's dark and enjoy them."

"Kindred spirits," agreed Danny. "They're special. The ones who keep them up until twelfth night are special."

"Let's go and find those special people," Saffie urged.

Danny's face brightened suddenly.

"We could have a party!" he exclaimed. "A Last Day of Christmas party. Just for the special people."

He caught a flicker of uncertainty in Saffie's eyes.

"Nothing big," he assured her. "Just coffee and mince pies and carols. We could shove an invitation through their letter-boxes when we go round later."

He rushed out of the room.

"Better get working on them," he called eagerly.

"I'll make some mince pies," laughed Saffie, heading for the kitchen.

"Thanks Saffie!" Danny shouted back. "You're a star!"

Saffie really was a star. She was great. Danny's decision to move in with her was the best one he had ever made.

That wasn't to say they were a couple. There was nothing romantic going on, and there was no deep and meaningful relationship. Danny and Saffie were simply two people who got on well together and shared a house for convenience and companionship.

Saffie was ambivalent about Christmas. She could take it or leave it. However she understood how important Christmas was to Danny and so she threw herself into it for his sake. He knew this and he loved her for it. Yes, Saffie was great. Saffie was a star.

Danny kept the invitations simple. Apart from anything else, there wasn't time to come up with an elaborate design. They needed to be ready for the evening.

He had a sudden disturbing thought and scurried to the kitchen to ask Saffie's advice.

"What about people who haven't got their decorations on show?" he said anxiously. "Perhaps there are people waiting for twelfth night but I don't know about them because their decorations are in a part of the house where I can't see them. I'll be missing out kindred spirits who deserve to be included."

Saffie looked up contemplatively from her bag of flour.

"Well …," she began, considering her words carefully. "If they don't have their decorations on show they're probably more private about what they're doing, aren't they?"

Danny nodded warily, hopefully.

"So …," continued Saffie. "We're okay sticking to the ones we know about because they're the ones who like to share their celebrations with others. The ones who keep their decorations out of sight … well, they might be into it or they might not. We have no way of knowing, but they're being private about it, so it's perfectly reasonable to leave them to their own private way of doing things."

She paused for breath. Danny was weighing up her comments.

"You're right," he concluded, satisfied, making his way back to the computer. "We'll stick to the ones who make a public statement about it."

Saffie smiled to herself and returned to her baking.

It was a chilly, drizzly evening and not at all pleasant for a walk around the block. There were so few lights and trees on show that it was really quite depressing, even for Saffie.

"Look!" exclaimed Danny crossly. "*They've* still got their lights up but they haven't bothered to switch them on. They could at least take them down if they're not going to switch them on anymore."

"Perhaps they're out," suggested Saffie. "Come on. Chin up. There are still a few decorations around. And maybe those people will come to our party."

She hoped upon hope they *would* come to the party. The last thing Danny needed was to be rejected and have his final day of Christmas celebration thwarted.

As if Danny had read her mind he stopped walking abruptly and grabbed her arm urgently.

"They *will* come, won't they, Saffie?" he pleaded.

Saffie sighed.

"We'll have to wait and see," she said softly, resisting with difficulty the temptation to offer him false assurances just to soothe him in that anxious moment. It wouldn't be fair to him in the long-run to make promises she was powerless to keep.

The kindred spirits had been invited to turn up at 7.30pm on January 5th. Danny hadn't requested them to RSVP, fearing that such a demand would put pressure on them and deter them.

This, of course, meant that he would have to endure an agonising twenty-four hours – almost – of wondering, hoping and dreading.

Would they come? Would it be a resounding success? Or a miserable, soul-destroying failure? Only time would tell.

Danny spent the next day fluctuating between buoyancy and despondency, flitting between making exciting preparations and lying forlornly on his bed tormenting himself with the expectation that it was all about to go horribly wrong.

Saffie considered calling secretly on the kindred spirits and giving them a little emotional prod in the right direction, but decided against it. It would be a betrayal of Danny's trust. If he ever found out his kindred spirits had been coerced into attending his party he would be devastated. He needed them to come because they *wanted* to come and for no other reason.

Oh, how Saffie hoped they *wanted* to come!

As 7.30pm drew near Danny and Saffie became increasingly agitated. Saffie hid her misgivings behind a mask of cheerfulness and positivity.

"You know, if they *don't* come it's probably just because they already had other plans," she chirped at regular intervals. "It was short notice. So even if they *don't* come it won't because they don't like the idea of a Last Day of Christmas party."

Danny didn't even attempt to hide *his* misgivings.

"What have I done, Saffie?" he cried at twenty past seven. "I've just opened myself up to getting hurt, haven't I? They *won't* come and I'll feel worse than ever."

They sat in silence for a moment. Everything was ready. Plates of mince pies were poised tantalisingly on a small table. The kettle had boiled, and mugs were set out on a tray ready to be filled with coffee or tea. Extra chairs had been crowded into the sitting-room and arranged in a friendly fashion. A CD of popular Christmas carols was waiting to be played and sung along to.

They just needed some guests. Would anybody come? It was almost 7.30. Saffie couldn't bear to look at Danny's dejected face.

The doorbell rang, making them both jump. They exchanged questioning glances. Guests? Dare they hope?

Danny couldn't bring himself to go to the door, so Saffie went to investigate on her own.

Danny heard animated voices and then Saffie led a man and a young girl into the room. Their faces were familiar to Danny, although he wasn't acquainted with them.

"We were just fancying a bit more Christmas, weren't we, love?" proclaimed the man, ruffling his daughter's hair.

The girl nodded self-consciously, her eyes scanning the room.

The doorbell rang again. This time Danny answered it. It was a middle-aged couple from further up the road.

"Number sixteen," they introduced themselves simultaneously.

"Those mince pies look good," added the man.

A few minutes later an elderly lady joined the gathering. She lived alone and had spent Christmas quietly and sombrely. Receiving an unexpected invitation to a Last Day of Christmas party had lifted her spirits and warmed her heart.

"Your Christmas tree is *beautiful!*" she enthused, bouncing into the room with surprising alacrity. "And I'm so touched that you invited me to your party. Just when I was feeling as if no one in the whole world really cared about me you made me feel loved again. Thank you."

Danny confirmed her house number and made a mental note to visit her regularly. He would probably have to take Saffie with him the first few times. He didn't want anyone suspecting him of preying on a vulnerable female.

It struck him with a sudden rush of intense compassion that people needed to be cared about *all* the time and not just at Christmas.

Danny noticed with pleasure that the young girl and elderly lady gravitated towards each other and quickly became a twosome. They spent the whole evening chatting and laughing together. It was a joy to behold.

Kindred spirits, reflected Danny contentedly.

He sensed that this new friendship would blossom and lead to a lot more companionship for the lonely senior citizen in the future.

All too soon people started to take their leave, but it had been a fun evening and Danny was blissfully happy.

"This ought to be an annual event," congratulated the man from number sixteen as he led the way to the front door. "It's been great. Well done, lad."

Danny and Saffie waved off their guests and returned elatedly to the sitting-room.

"Thanks, Saffie," gushed Danny, giving her a big hug. "I couldn't have done it without you."

"And I *wouldn't* have done it without *you*," laughed Saffie.

40. So That Was That

So that was that. It's over now
It came and then it went
I feel a bit embarrassed when
I think how much I spent

I've eaten well, had lots of gifts
And dozed each afternoon
My *Thank You* notes are still unsent –
I'll write them sometime soon

I need to tidy up a bit
I haven't done that yet …
And give the house a thorough clean …
… Perhaps I'll just forget!

I feel quite sad. Depressed. Forlorn
I love the festive cheer
But Christmas time is over now
- Till later in the year

Other Titles By Helen M. Clarke

Mince Pies And Paper Chains
A collection of 22 rhyming poems, 12 short stories and 6 miscellaneous prose pieces, all on a Christmas theme.

The Christmas Love Tree
A gentle story with a Christian slant. Newly retired Geraldine is thoroughly enjoying her freedom and the chance to be self-indulgent, although she is becoming increasingly aware of an unsettling feeling of emptiness and aimlessness. When she offers to help two children with their entry for the local Christmas Tree Festival she has no idea what a profound impact her involvement with their Christmas Love Tree will have on her life.

"With Love And Best Wishes..."
An affectionate skit on the round-robin Christmas letter.

Christmas Uncancelled
A gentle Christmas story, suitable for children and adults. Christmas is going to be awful. Lynette's parents have gone on holiday and left her with old-fashioned Auntie Dorothy and pesky little Johnny. To make matters worse, the neighbours are acting strangely and Lynette is sure they're up to no good. Lynette prepares herself for a miserable time. She has no intention of even trying to enjoy herself. But will she really be able to stay grumpy throughout Christmas?

Life's Little Quirks
50 light-hearted rhyming poems.

Life's Wonders And Riches
40 rhyming, rhythmic poems - a mixture of light-hearted and serious - celebrating and reflecting on life.

Canine Confusions And Feline Frustrations

A cat and dog saga told through the animals' emails.

Rescue dog Scruff has just moved into a new home, where resident cat Cleopatra reigns supreme. To Scruff's surprise, Cleopatra doesn't seem particularly thrilled to have him around. As Scruff and Cleopatra try to come to terms with their new living arrangements, Scruff exchanges emails with worldly-wise Maxie, his friend from the Pound, while Cleopatra corresponds with her devoted sister Tallulah.

Charlie's A To Y

A dog's definitions in verse.

Verses For Greeting Cards

100 rhyming poems, with no copyright restrictions, for use in card making.

More Verses For Greeting Cards

A second collection of rhyming poems, with no copyright restrictions, for use in card making. A companion to the first collection.

Verses For Birthday And Christmas Cards

65 rhyming poems, with no copyright restrictions, for use in card making. There are 35 birthday verses (12 of which are for children) and 30 Christmas verses (6 for children).

Messages In Rhyme

Rhyming poems, with no copyright restrictions, for use in card making.

Another Move, Another Church
A series of rhyming, rhythmic poems depicting a year in the life of
a small English church, seen through the eyes of the minister's
teenage daughter.

Honest With God
Poems and reflections for worship and private devotions, focusing
on Life's Ups and Downs and Through the Year.

Noah Gets It Right
15 poems retelling Bible stories in a light-hearted, colloquial style.

Printed in Great Britain
by Amazon